KU-589-844

SUSAN EATON

DISSECTION GUIDES

II. THE DOGFISH

by

H. G. Q. ROWETT, M.A.

LECTURER AT THE COLLEGE OF TECHNOLOGY, PLYMOUTH

LONDON

JOHN MURRAY, 50 ALBEMARLE STREET, W.

First published 1950
Reprinted 1953
Reprinted 1956
Reprinted 1957
Reprinted 1960
Reprinted 1961
Reprinted 1964

DISSECTION GUIDES

by H. G. Q. ROWETT, M.A.

I.   THE FROG
II. THE DOGFISH
III. THE RAT
IV. THE RABBIT
V.   INVERTEBRATES

BY THE SAME AUTHOR

HISTOLOGY AND EMBRYOLOGY

BASIC ANATOMY AND PHYSIOLOGY

THE RAT AS A SMALL MAMMAL

GUIDE TO DISSECTION

MADE AND PRINTED IN GREAT BRITAIN
BY BUTLER AND TANNER LTD., FROME AND LONDON
AND PUBLISHED BY JOHN MURRAY (PUBLISHERS) LTD.

INTRODUCTION

This series of drawings is designed to aid dissection with the minimum of written instruction. In the dissection of the dogfish it is not always possible to show the exact position of the instruments for the making of every cut, because frequently a process of 'carving' is used, in which the tissue is sliced away little by little till the desired result is achieved. It is important not to cut off large pieces blindly.

The tissues of the dogfish are extremely tough. This dissection therefore tends to blunt the instruments very rapidly. It is a good rule to keep the finest scalpel and pair of scissors for delicate work and fine trimming only. Rub the scalpels on a sharpening-stone at frequent intervals.

Owing to the size of the dogfish, Figs. 1–23 are less than life-size. The student should make his drawings as large as, or even larger than, the dissection itself.

Each important structure is labelled when it first becomes visible, but not thereafter, unless necessary for the clarification of the instructions. No attempt is made to describe the form and relation of the parts.

The dogfish is dissected on a wooden board to which it is fixed by means of strong wooden or brass-handled dissecting pins.

CONTENTS

GENERAL DIRECTIONS FOR OPENING UP THE BODY CAVITY

The dogfish supplied for dissection is always in the preserved condition. The preservation is carried out either (*a*) by soaking the fish in formalin, or (*b*) by injection with formalin followed by soaking till required for use.

The rate of penetration of formalin is slow, therefore when the former method is used the dogfish is opened up to allow the preservative to reach the internal structures before they have time to decay. This preliminary treatment includes the removal of a small portion of the roof of the skull in order to open the brain-case, a small central part of the pectoral girdle to open the pericardium, and the greater part of the ventral wall of the abdomen to expose the viscera. At the same time the tail is usually cut off, as it is not required during the dissection and would occupy a great deal of storage room.

If this is the condition of the fish the student can proceed directly to Fig. 4.

The injection method of preservation has the advantage that the viscera are not displaced or damaged during storage or transport, but it has the disadvantage that the blood is forced from the efferent branchial vessels, rendering them completely colourless.

If the dogfish is preserved in this way the tail only is removed. The body cavity must be opened up as shown in Figs. 1–5 before dissection of the alimentary canal, urinogenital system and abdominal blood-vessels.

Note. Unless otherwise stated, a male fish is shown in the diagrams. The female differs from it in the absence of claspers and in the form of the cloaca.

OPENING UP THE BODY CAVITY

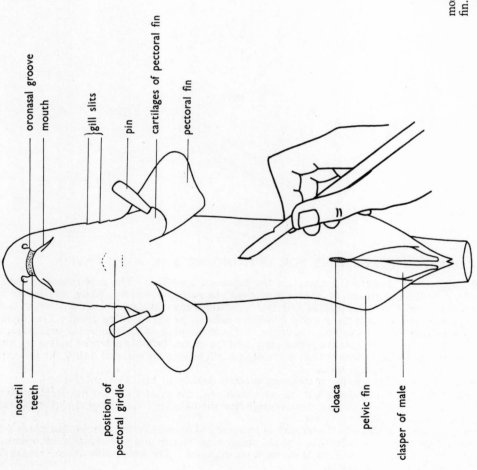

nostril

teeth

position of
pectoral girdle

cloaca

pelvic fin

clasper of male

oronasal groove

mouth

}gill slits

pin

cartilages of pectoral fin

pectoral fin

Fig. 1

Place the dogfish on the dissecting-board ventral side upper-most and pin through the CARTILAGENOUS PART of each pectoral fin. The pins must be long and strong. NOTE. If the pins are inserted through the region of the fin rays the fins tear when strain is put upon them.

Make a small incision in the skin in the mid-ventral line by means of a scalpel. The skin is firmly fixed to the underlying muscle which will therefore usually be cut also. DO NOT CUT DEEPLY at first.

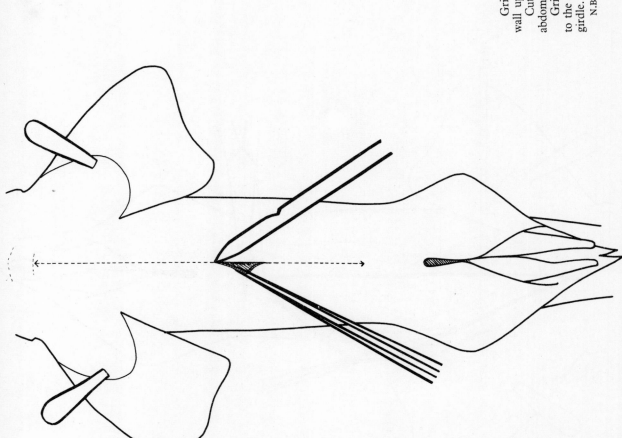

Fig. 2

Grip the edge of the slit made in Fig. I and pull the body wall up slightly.

Cut with a scalpel, using small upward strokes until the abdominal cavity is perforated.

Grip the cut edge more firmly and continue the slit forwards to the level of the pectoral girdle and backwards to the pelvic girdle. The girdles can be felt through the skin.

N.B. Be careful not to cut the abdominal viscera.

OPENING UP THE BODY CAVITY

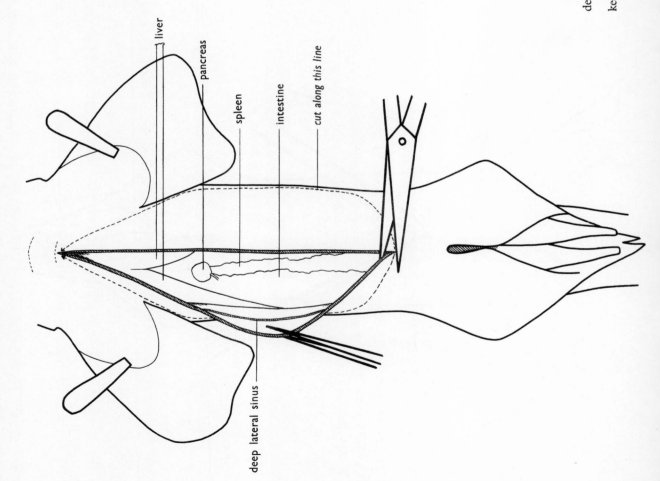

liver

pancreas

spleen

intestine

cut along this line

deep lateral sinus

Fig. 3

Hold aside the ventral part of the body wall and look for the deep lateral sinus.

Cut away the skin and muscle of the abdominal wall together, keeping the lateral part of the cut just ventral to the above sinus.

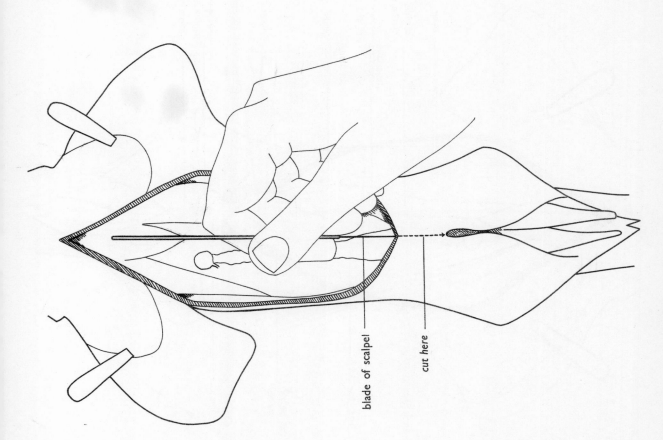

blade of scalpel

cut here

Fig. 4

Holding the scalpel as shown, cut the body wall back to the cloaca. Cut through the pelvic girdle at the same time so that the abdominal cavity is opened to its posterior limit.

Note. If preferred, the board may be turned and scissors be used for this cut.

2

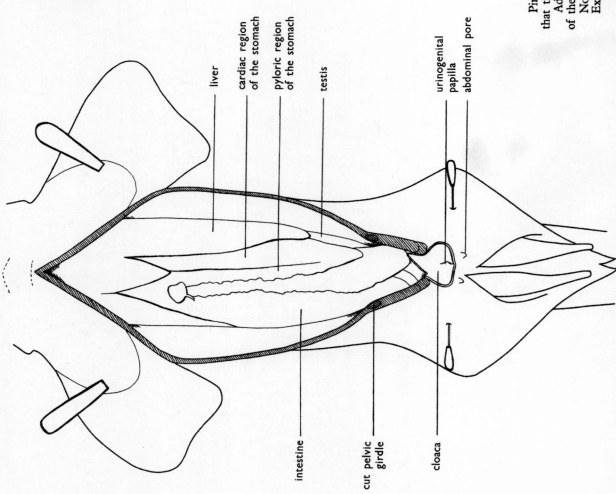

liver

cardiac region
of the stomach

pyloric region
of the stomach

testis

urinogenital
papilla

abdominal pore

intestine

cut pelvic
girdle

cloaca

Fig. 5

Pin the pelvic fins to the lateral musculature in such a way
that the cloaca is stretched open as shown.

Adjust the pins through the pectoral fins so that the sides
of the abdominal wall are drawn apart laterally.

Note. The form of the female cloaca is shown in Fig. 20.
Examine and DRAW the viscera in situ.

THE ALIMENTARY CANAL

The abdominal portions of the alimentary canal and their associated glands should be displayed as shown in Figs. 6–8.

The dissection of the anterior parts of the canal must be postponed if the venous sinuses and afferent branchial arteries are required later. The method of display of the buccal cavity and pharynx is shown in Figs. 42 and 43.

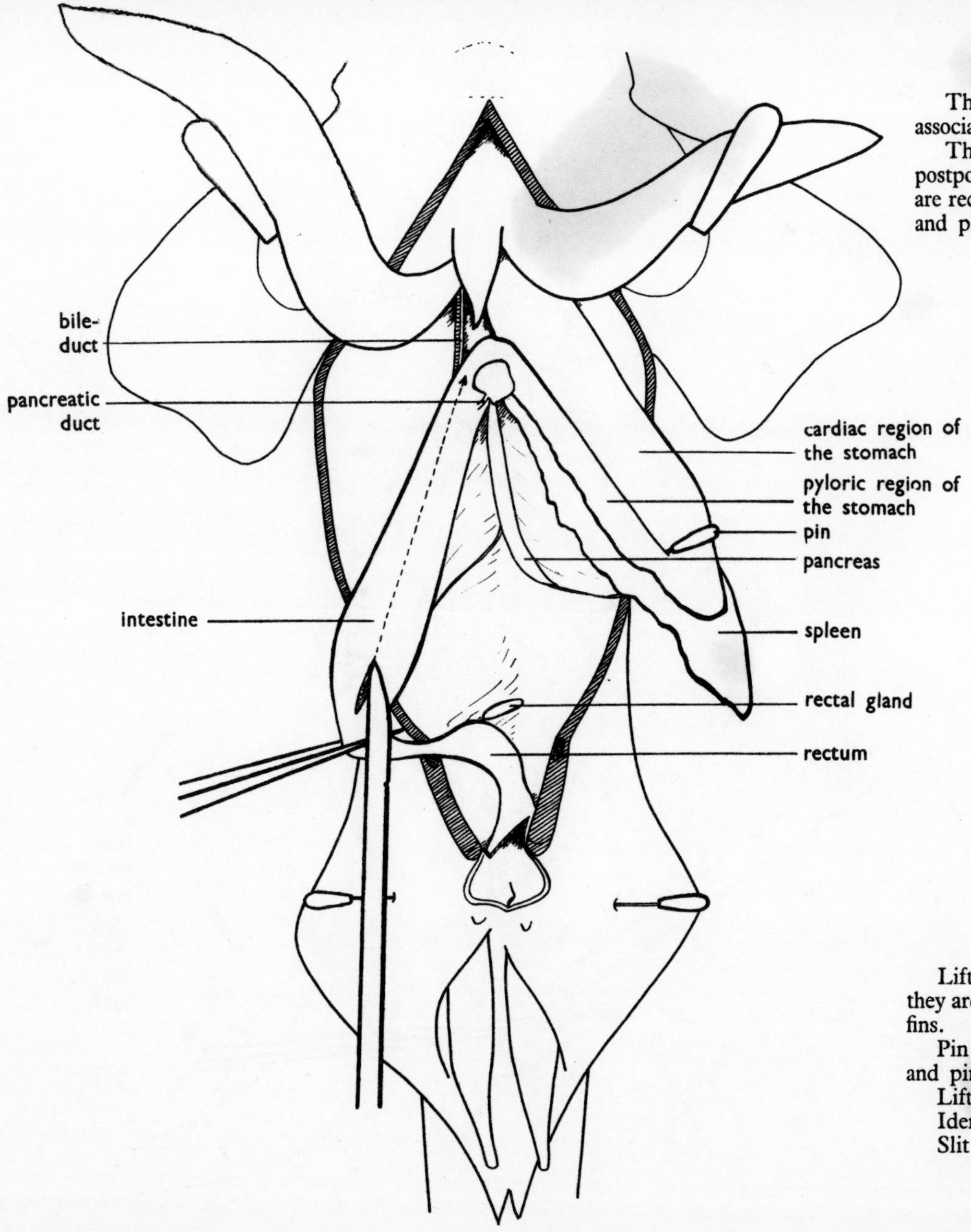

Fig. 6

Lift the right and left liver lobes and place them so that they are supported as shown by the pins which hold the pectoral fins.

Pin the stomach to your right, using a small dissecting-pin and pinning to the body wall.

Lift the intestine to the left.

Identify the parts shown in the diagram.

Slit up the ventral side of the intestine.

THE ALIMENTARY CANAL

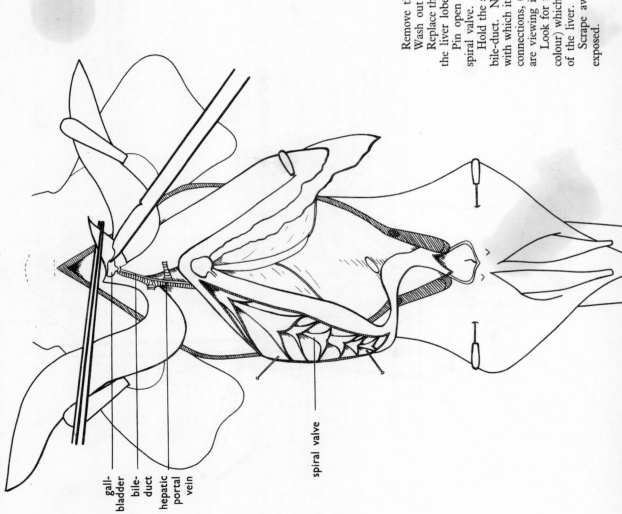

gall-
bladder
bile-
duct
hepatic
portal
vein

spiral valve

Remove the dogfish from the board.

Wash out the contents of the intestine.

Replace the dogfish on the board. Fix with pins and adjust the liver lobes as before.

Pin open the intestine as shown in order to display the spiral valve.

Hold the small median lobe of the liver aside and trace the bile-duct. Notice that it lies close to the hepatic portal vein with which it is often confused. It can be identified by (a) its connections, (b) its whiter colour, and (c) the fact that as you are viewing it, it lies to the right of the vein.

Look for the small portion of the gall-bladder (greenish in colour) which usually shows on the surface of the median lobe of the liver.

Scrape away the liver tissue till the gall-bladder is fully exposed.

Fig. 7

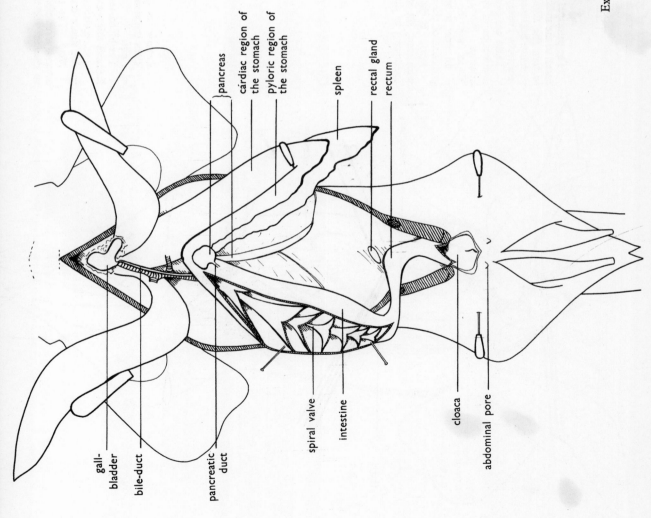

gall-bladder

bile-duct

pancreatic duct

pancreas

cardiac region of the stomach

pyloric region of the stomach

spleen

rectal gland

rectum

spiral valve

intestine

cloaca

abdominal pore

Fig. 8

Examine and DRAW the completed dissection.

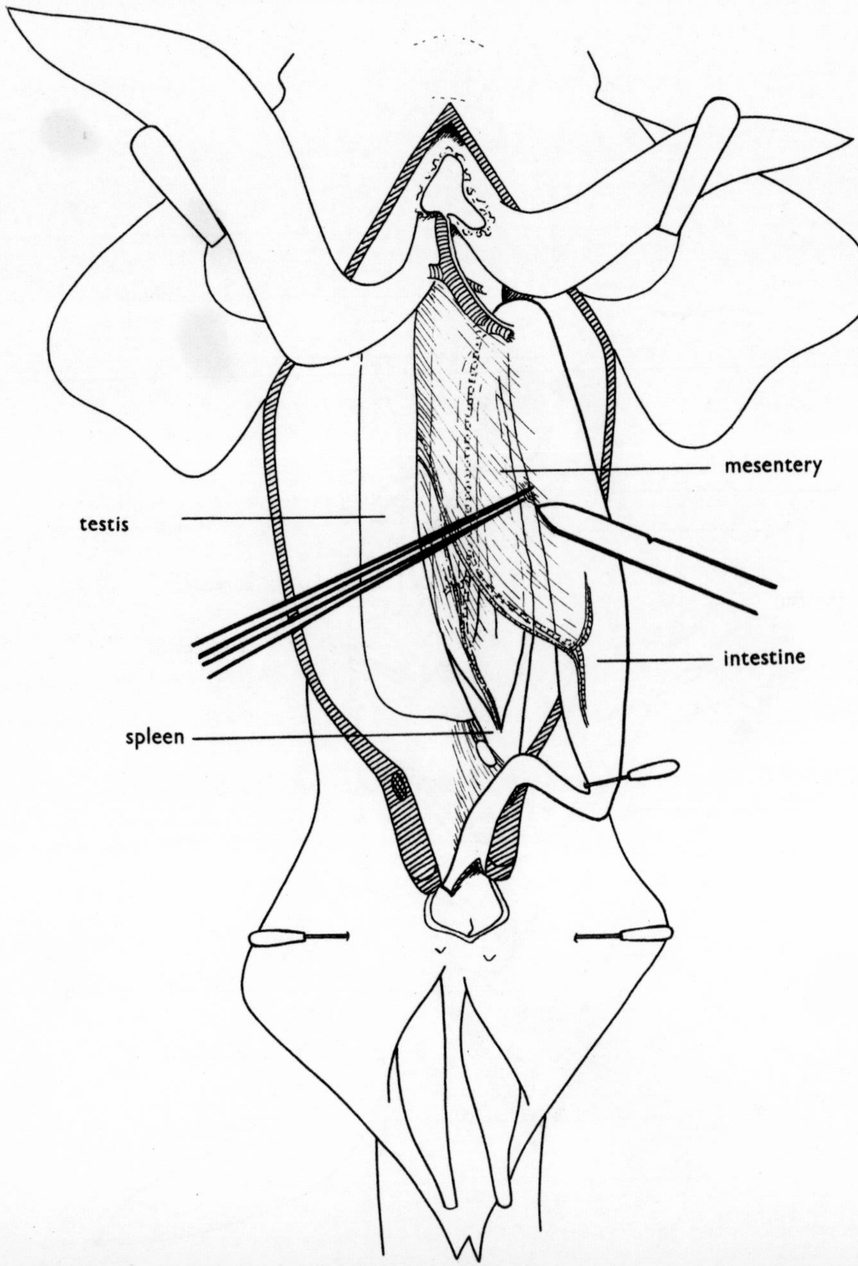

THE ARTERIES AND VEINS OF THE ALIMENTARY CANAL

The principal blood-vessels to and from the alimentary canal lie dorsal to the structures which they serve. To see them it is necessary to turn the alimentary canal over. Remember that your drawing therefore becomes largely a dorsal rather than a ventral view and that structures usually seen to your right are now left, and vice versa.

There are considerable individual differences in the detail of the distribution of the blood-vessels on the surface of the stomach and intestine. No attempt has therefore been made to show them. Notice how the arteries and veins accompany one another.

In order to see all the vessels clearly it is necessary to adjust the positions of the organs carefully.

NOTE. If the cardiac region of the stomach is much distended with food, slit it open ventrally and wash out the contents before attempting to display the blood-vessels.

Fig. 9a. Male

Remove the pins from the stomach and intestine.
Turn the stomach and intestine over and hold in place by means of a pin.
The blood-vessels do not show clearly because of the mesentery.
Remove this mesentery carefully, stripping off small pieces at a time. N.B. WATCH FOR THE BLOOD-VESSELS indicated by the dotted lines in this figure and those shown in Fig. 10.

NOTE. The crossing of the lienogastric and anterior mesenteric arteries takes place within the mesentery proper and there is no need to displace the mesorchium.

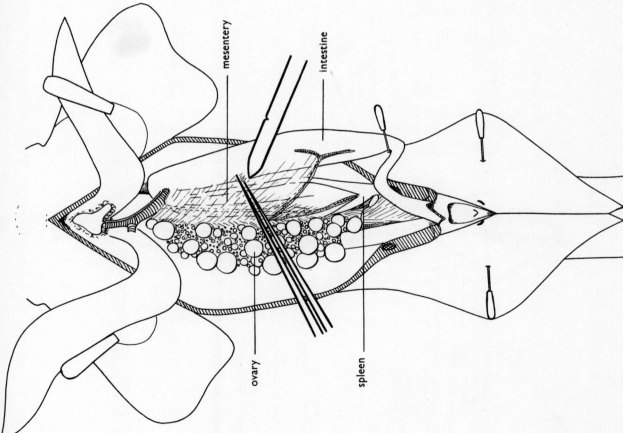

Fig. 9b. Female

As for Fig. 9a, but note that the mesentery is attached to the mesovarium and the crossing over of the lienogastric and anterior mesenteric arteries takes place within the latter. It is important not to cut the mesovarium if the urinogenital system is to be displayed later.

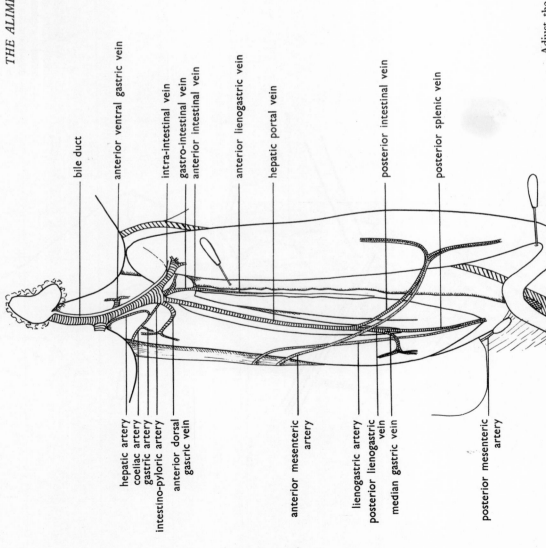

Fig. 10a. Male

Adjust the position of the alimentary canal, using pins if necessary.

Identify the blood-vessels shown and DRAW.

bile duct

anterior ventral gastric vein

intra-intestinal vein

gastro-intestinal vein

anterior intestinal vein

anterior lienogastric vein

hepatic portal vein

posterior intestinal vein

posterior splenic vein

hepatic artery

coeliac artery

gastric artery

intestino-pyloric artery

anterior dorsal gasric vein

anterior mesenteric artery

lienogastric artery

posterior lienogastric vein

median gastric vein

posterior mesenteric artery

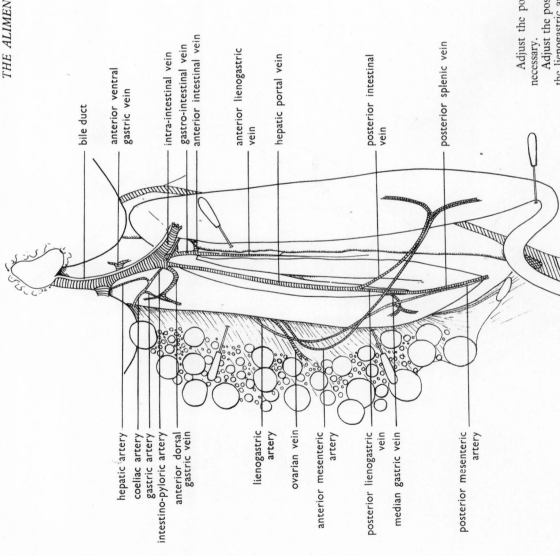

bile duct

anterior ventral
gastric vein

intra-intestinal vein
gastro-intestinal vein
anterior intestinal vein

anterior lienogastric
vein

hepatic portal vein

posterior intestinal
vein

posterior splenic vein

hepatic artery
coeliac artery
gastric artery
intestino-pyloric artery
anterior dorsal
gastric vein

lienogastric
artery

ovarian vein

anterior mesenteric
artery

posterior lienogastric
vein
median gastric vein

posterior mesenteric
artery

Fig. 10b. Female

Adjust the position of the alimentary canal, using pins if
necessary.
Adjust the position of the ovary so that the crossing over of
the lienogastric and anterior mesenteric arteries shows clearly.
Identify the blood-vessels shown and DRAW.

17

3

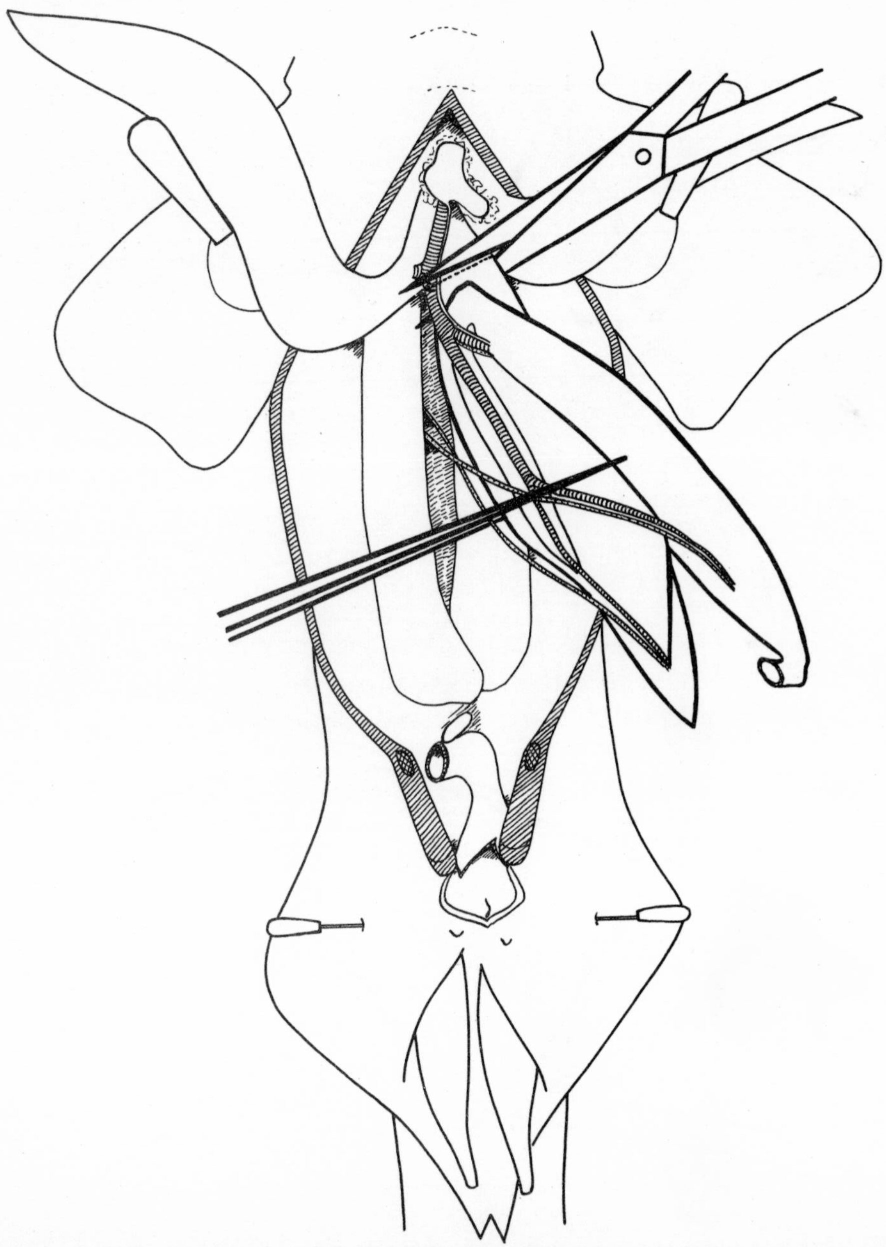

THE URINOGENITAL SYSTEM

(a) MALE

In the male dogfish the kidneys and the ducts of the urinogenital system (except the vasa efferentia) lie against the dorsal wall of the abdomen and are covered over by a tough layer of peritoneum. The testes are, however, suspended freely in the body cavity by a relatively delicate mesorchium within the anterior part of which run the vasa efferentia. The mesorchium tears easily and therefore the testes are often found to be lying loose when the specimen is received. Before drawing the completed dissection the student should place the testes in the positions shown in Fig. 19 and should indicate the vasa efferentia by dotted lines only. The exact position of these ducts and the form of the testes vary considerably.

Remove any pins which are holding the alimentary canal.
Grip the alimentary canal as shown.
Cut through the rectum close to the rectal gland.
Cut through the oesophagus, the bile-duct and the hepatic portal vein. Cut through the lienogastric and anterior mesenteric arteries.

Remove the stomach and intestine, taking the pancreas and spleen with them.

Fig. 11

18

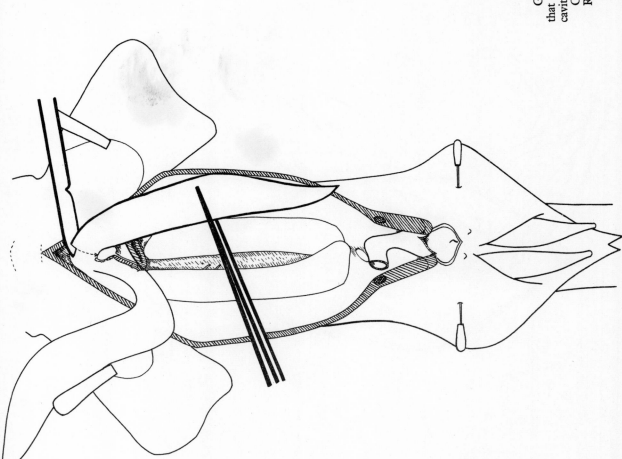

Fig. 12

Grip one lobe of the liver and pull it gently towards you so that the anterior boundary is drawn out of the abdominal cavity.

Cut away the liver lobe as completely as possible.

Repeat to remove the other lobe of the liver.

THE URINOGENITAL SYSTEM

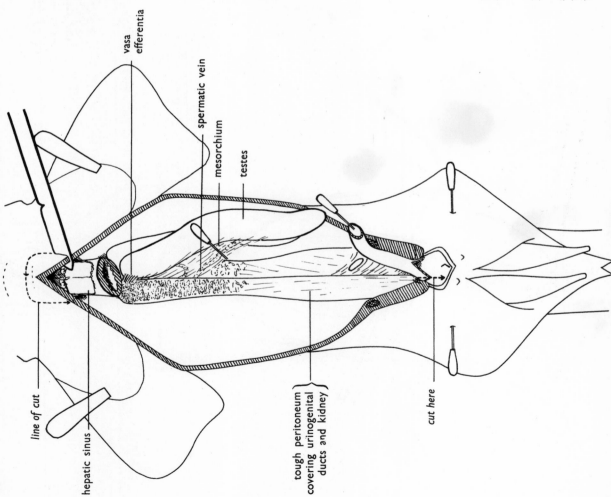

vasa
efferentia

spermatic vein

mesorchium

testes

line of cut

hepatic sinus

tough peritoneum
covering urinogenital
ducts and kidney

cut here

Fig. 13

Lay both testes over to one side and hold in place
by means of a pin placed as shown, BESIDE not through
the testes.

Pin aside the rectum.

Slit down the side of the cloaca to the posterior
limit of the abdominal cavity.

Carve away a further portion of the wall of the
anterior end of the abdominal cavity, cutting through
the cartilage of the pectoral girdle at the same time so
that the pericardial cavity is opened.

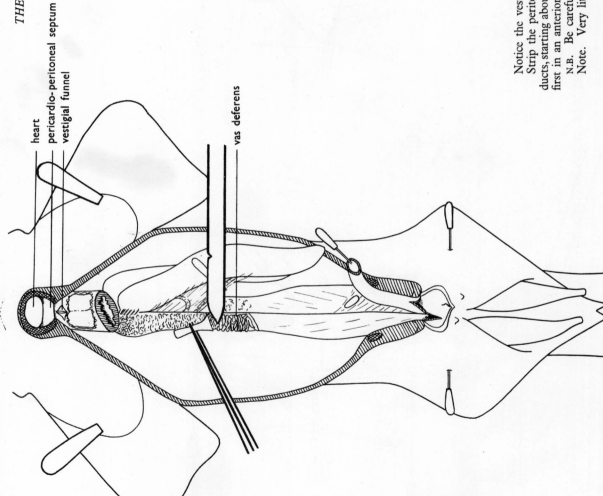

heart

pericardio-peritoneal septum

vestigial funnel

vas deferens

Fig. 14

Notice the vestigial oviducal funnel.
Strip the peritoneum from the surface of the urinogenital
ducts, starting about halfway down the body cavity and working
first in an anterior and then in a posterior direction.
N.B. Be careful not to damage the ducts.
Note. Very little of the kidney is visible at this stage.

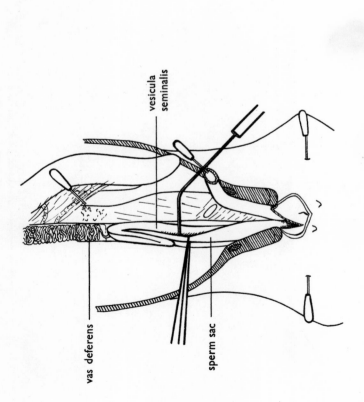

Fig. 15

Using a seeker, gently separate the sperm sac from the vesicula seminalis to which it is attached by very soft connective tissue.

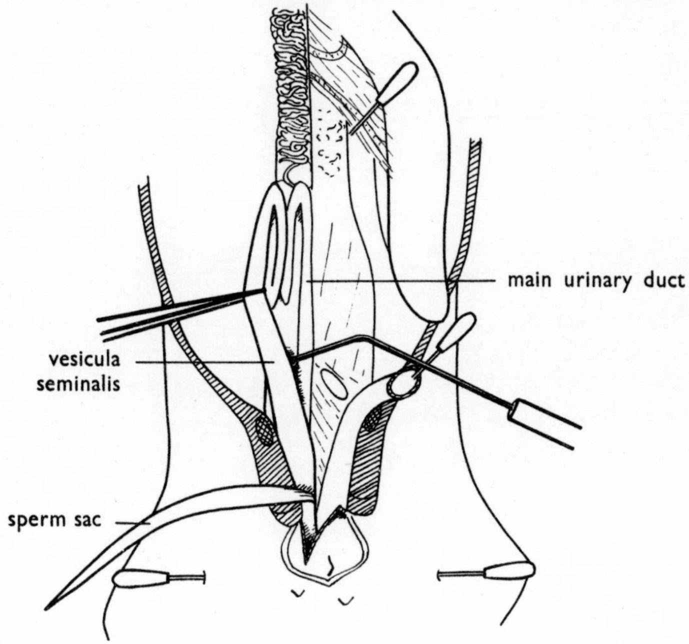

Fig. 16

Similarly loosen the vesicula seminalis from the main urinary duct and the surface of the kidney.

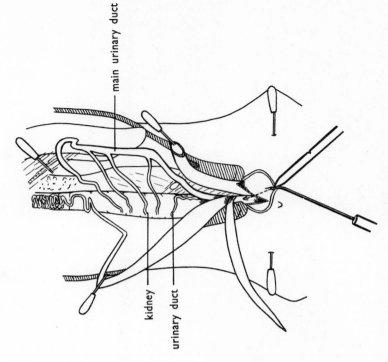

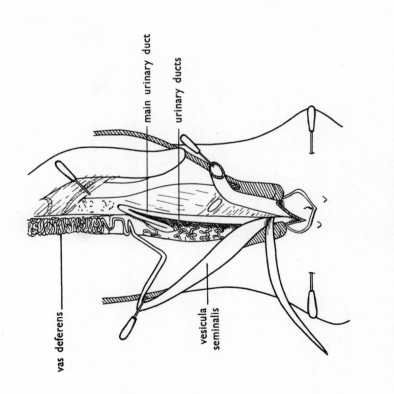

Fig. 17

Trace the connection between the vesicula seminalis and the vas deferens, loosening the connective tissue as required. Pin the vesicula seminalis aside.

VERY GENTLY loosen the main urinary duct and its tributaries from the kidney.

N.B. The urinary ducts are VERY DELICATE and utmost care must be taken when endeavouring to loosen them from the connective tissue.

Fig. 18

Display the urinary ducts as shown.

Insert a seeker through the urinogenital aperture into the urinogenital sinus and thence into the sperm sac.

Use the seeker as a guide to make a cut along the line indicated.

N.B. Keep the point of the scalpel as close to the seeker as possible and make a series of short cuts.

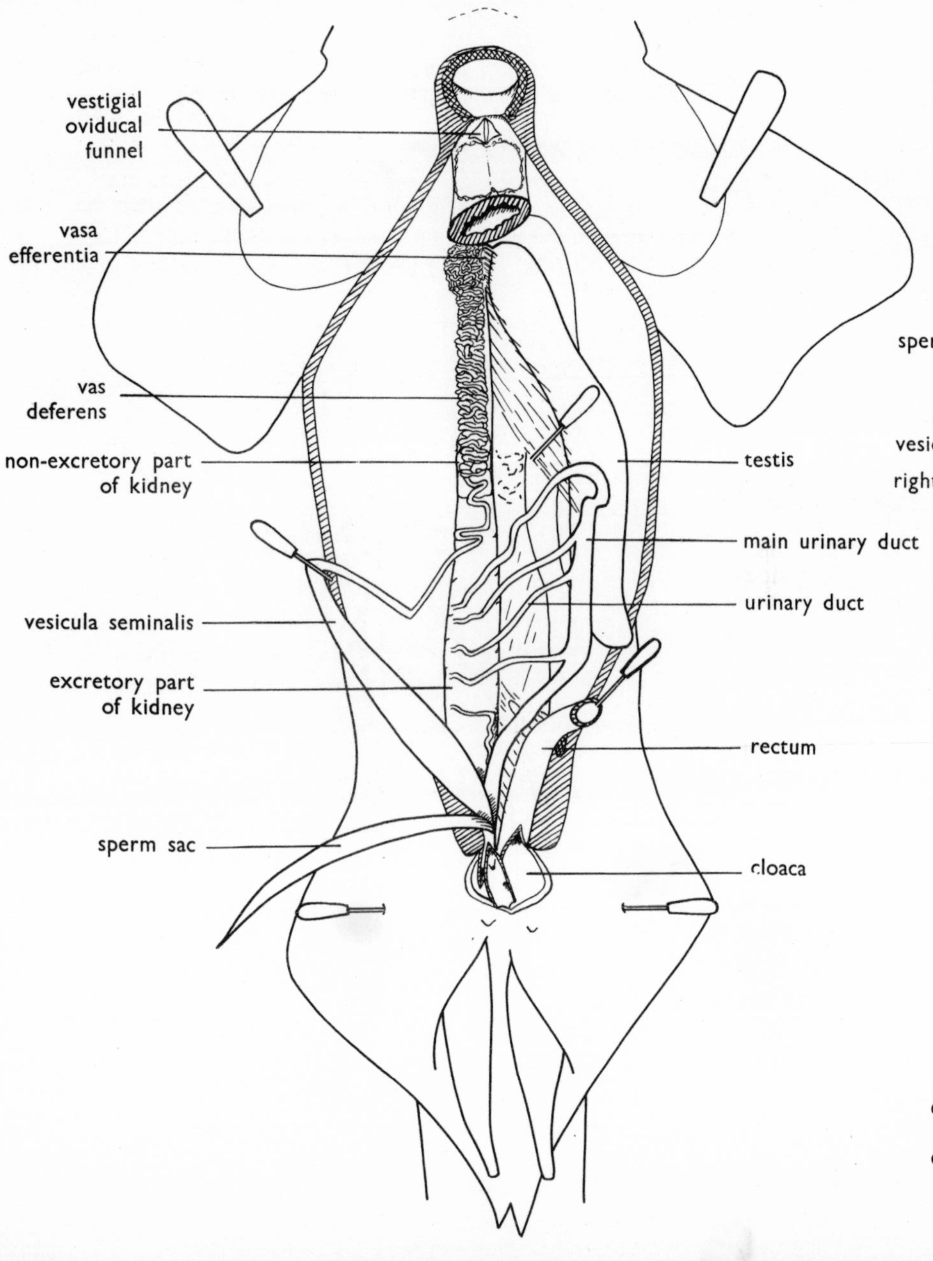

THE URINOGENITAL SYSTEM

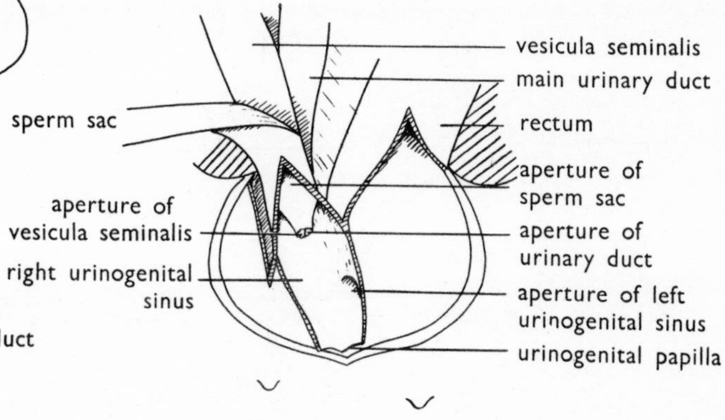

vesicula seminalis
main urinary duct
rectum
aperture of sperm sac
aperture of urinary duct
aperture of left urinogenital sinus
urinogenital papilla

sperm sac
aperture of vesicula seminalis
right urinogenital sinus

Inset

testis
main urinary duct
urinary duct
rectum
cloaca

vestigial oviducal funnel
vasa efferentia
vas deferens
non-excretory part of kidney
vesicula seminalis
excretory part of kidney
sperm sac

Fig. 19

Notice the apertures of the vesicula seminalis and urinary duct.

The inset is an enlargement of the cloacal region to show detail.

DRAW the completed dissection.

24

THE URINOGENITAL SYSTEM

(b) FEMALE

The peritoneum varies considerably in thickness. Where it forms the mesovarium it is very fine and must be handled carefully, especially when the ovary is ripe. N.B. There is only ONE ovary, although there are two oviducts.

The membrane supporting the oviduct is considerably tougher, while that covering the median parts of the kidneys is very tough indeed. The latter merges with a thin covering over the urinary sinus. It is necessary to remove the covering of the median part of the kidney without damaging the urinary sinus, which can then be laid aside to display the kidney and urinary ducts.

In some specimens there is a large swelling of the oviduct posterior to the shell gland. It indicates the presence of an egg in its case ready for oviposition, and can be examined by slitting the oviduct open. The egg itself is usually in a bad state of preservation owing to the slow penetration of the formalin through the horny capsule.

In specimens of young dogfish the aperture of the genital sinus is covered over by the membranous hymen. It usually tears a little when the cloaca is opened.

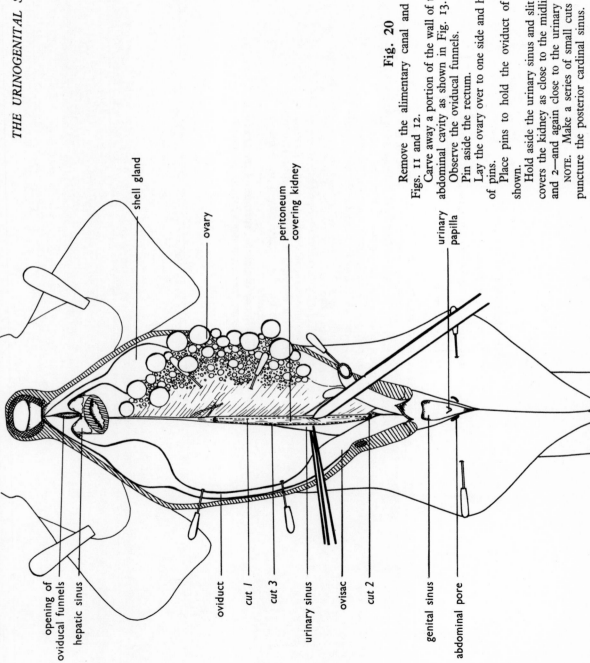

Fig. 20

Remove the alimentary canal and liver as indicated in Figs. 11 and 12.

Carve away a portion of the wall of the anterior end of the abdominal cavity as shown in Fig. 13.

Observe the oviducal funnels.

Pin aside the rectum.

Lay the ovary over to one side and hold in place by means of pins.

Place pins to hold the oviduct of the opposite side as shown.

Hold aside the urinary sinus and slit the peritoneum which covers the kidney as close to the midline as possible—cuts 1 and 2—and again close to the urinary sinus—cut 3.

NOTE. Make a series of small cuts and be careful not to puncture the posterior cardinal sinus.

THE URINOGENITAL SYSTEM

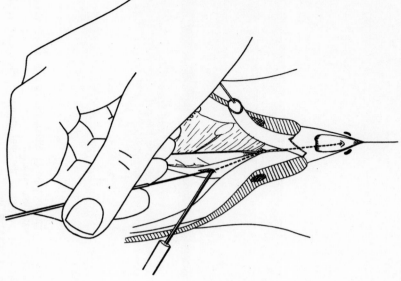

posterior cardinal sinus

urinary duct

Fig. 21

Lift the urinary sinus and gently loosen the soft connective tissue which binds it to the kidney. WATCH FOR THE FOUR OR FIVE VERY DELICATE URINARY DUCTS.

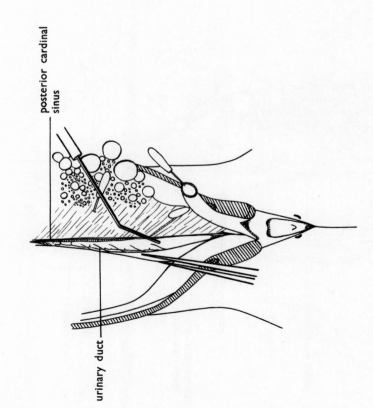

Fig. 22

Make a small slit in the urinary sinus.
Insert a seeker into the urinary sinus as shown.
Cut with a scalpel along the line indicated, using the seeker as a guide.
NOTE. This cut will pass between the two oviducts, through the roof of the genital sinus and through the cloaca. It should open the urinary sinus and show its connection with the urinary papilla.
Slit the urinary sinus open to its anterior limit.

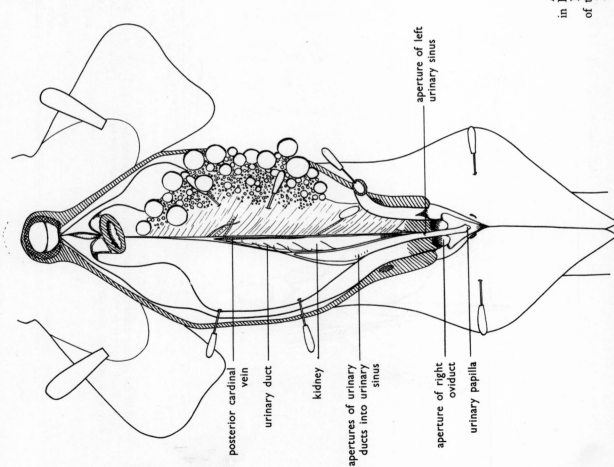

posterior cardinal
vein

urinary duct

kidney

apertures of urinary
ducts into urinary
sinus

aperture of right
oviduct

urinary papilla

aperture of left
urinary sinus

Fig. 23

Adjust the pins through the pelvic fins so that the slit made
in Fig. 22 is stretched widely.
Notice the openings of the oviducts and of the urinary sinus
of the undissected side.
DRAW the completed dissection.

28

THE VENOUS SINUSES

Students are not generally required to make a complete dissection of the venous sinuses. Such a dissection involves cutting in such a way that the arteries and nerves are difficult to dissect afterwards.

It is usually sufficient to open up the sinus venosus and the ductus Cuvieri of one side and to identify the apertures of the principal sinuses into them.

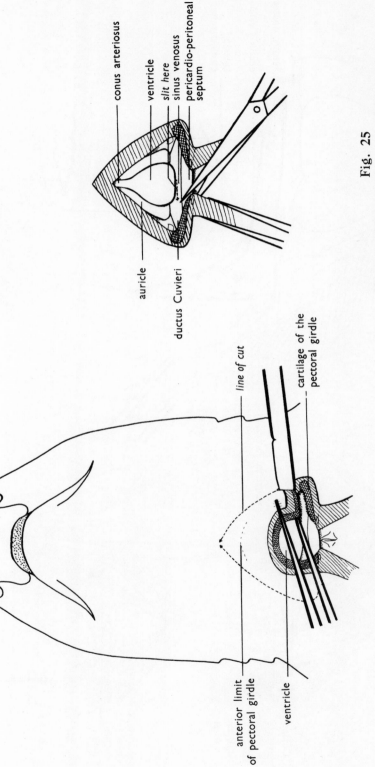

Fig. 25

Notice the heart within the pericardial cavity.

Using scissors, cut the pericardio-peritoneal septum close to the body wall on one side only. Extend the cut to the lateral limit of the pericardial cavity.

Adjust the pins through the pectoral fins so that the posterior boundary of the pericardial cavity is stretched.

Make a slit in the sinus venosus.

Labels (Fig. 25): conus arteriosus, ventricle, slit here, sinus venosus, pericardio-peritoneal septum, auricle, ductus Cuvieri

Fig. 24

Carve away the floor of the pericardial cavity, cutting first laterally and then forwards as shown.

N.B. Take care that the point of the scalpel is within the pericardial cavity at the beginning of each stroke.

Labels (Fig. 24): line of cut, cartilage of the pectoral girdle, anterior limit of pectoral girdle, ventricle

29

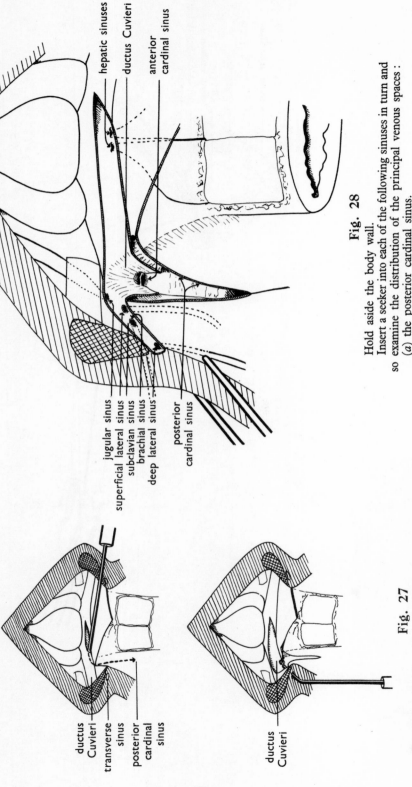

THE VENOUS SINUSES

Fig. 26

Insert a seeker into the slit in the sinus venosus and well down through the ductus Cuvieri.

Cut to follow the seeker through the ductus Cuvieri and into the posterior cardinal sinus.

Fig. 27

Insert a seeker into the transverse sinus and through the subclavian sinus into the ductus Cuvieri.

Cut following the seeker and clear away the tissue on either side of the opened sinus.

If necessary, open the sinus venosus further to show the apertures of the hepatic sinuses.

Fig. 28

Hold aside the body wall.

Insert a seeker into each of the following sinuses in turn and so examine the distribution of the principal venous spaces :

(*a*) the posterior cardinal sinus.
(*b*) the anterior cardinal sinus.
(*c*) the inferior jugular sinus.
(*d*) the deep lateral sinus.
(*e*) the brachial sinus.
(*f*) the superficial lateral sinus.
(*g*) the hepatic sinus.
DRAW.

30

THE ARTERIAL SYSTEM

(a) THE VENTRAL AORTA AND AFFERENT BRANCHIAL ARTERIES

This part of the arterial system lies ventral to the pharynx. The dissection is made easier if the latter be distended by a small cylinder of cork or wood about 2 inches long by $\frac{1}{2}$ inch in diameter. Insert the cylinder into the mouth and push it well down the pharynx. Do not let any of it remain between the jaws.

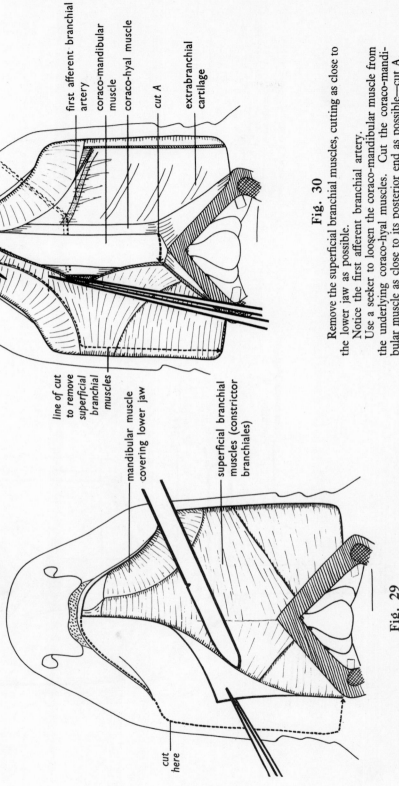

Fig. 29

Remove the skin from the ventral surface between the mouth and the heart.
Notice the superficial branchial muscles and the mandibular muscles.

Fig. 30

Remove the superficial branchial muscles, cutting as close to the lower jaw as possible.
Notice the first afferent branchial artery.
Use a seeker to loosen the coraco-mandibular muscle from the underlying coraco-hyal muscles. Cut the coraco-mandibular muscle as close to its posterior end as possible—cut A.

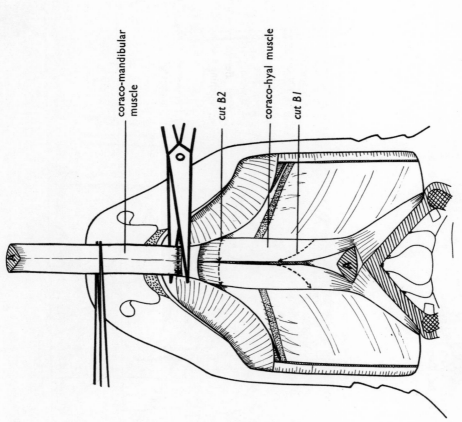

coraco-mandibular
muscle

cut B2

coraco-hyal muscle

cut B1

Fig. 31

Turn the coraco-mandibular muscle forwards. Free it carefully to its insertion in the ligament between the mandibles. Cut as indicated.

Remove the coraco-hyal muscles in a similar way—cuts B1 and B2.

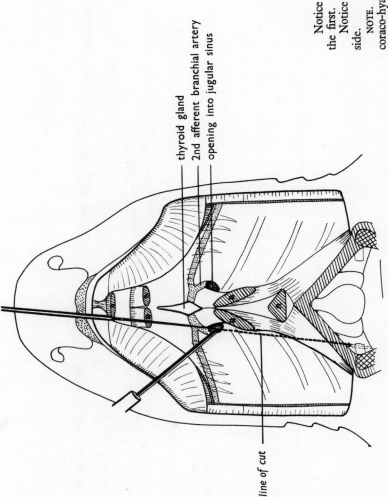

thyroid gland

2nd afferent branchial artery

opening into jugular sinus

line of cut

Fig. 32

Notice the second afferent branchial artery branching from the first.

Notice the opening of the inferior jugular sinus on either side.

NOTE. This sinus is usually opened by the removal of the coraco-hyal muscles, but if it is not visible, gently loosen the connective tissue along the line of the second afferent branchial artery.

Insert a seeker into the sinus CAREFULLY. N.B. DO NOT USE FORCE. The seeker will follow the correct line of the sinus easily.

Use a scalpel held as shown in Fig. 4 to cut through all the tissue ventral to the sinus, keeping the seeker as a guide.

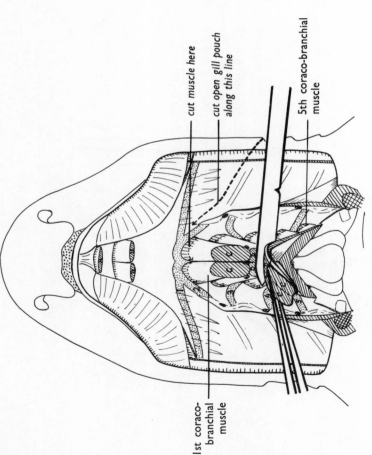

Fig. 33

Notice the third, fourth and fifth afferent branchial arteries (3, 4 and 5 in diagram) crossing the roof of the jugular sinus. Notice also the coraco-branchial muscles.

Remove the thyroid gland.

Cut away the block of tissue from which the coraco-mandibular, coraco-hyal and coraco-branchial muscles originate by making a horizontal cut as shown. By doing so, the cut ends of the five pairs of coraco-branchial muscles C, D, [E, F, G] become exposed. Loosen these muscles from one another, watching for the ventral aorta in the midline and for the afferent branchial arteries between the second and third, third and fourth, and fourth and fifth pairs of muscles respectively.

Cut all the coraco-branchial muscle-blocks as short as possible—see Fig. 34, C, D, E, F, G.

Insert one blade of the scissors through the first gill slit and cut the floor of the gill pouch along the line shown.

1st coraco-branchial muscle

cut muscle here

cut open gill pouch along this line

5th coraco-branchial muscle

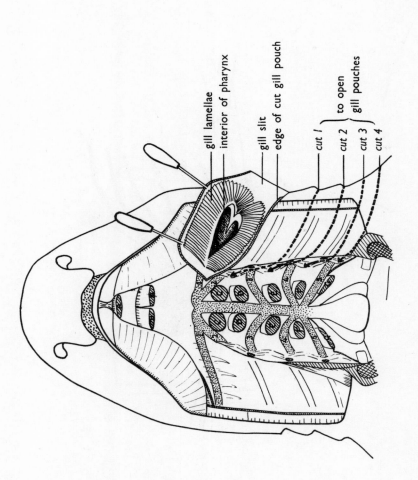

gill lamellae
interior of pharynx

gill slit
edge of cut gill pouch

cut 1
cut 2 } to open
cut 3 } gill pouches
cut 4

Fig. 34

This is the best stage for an examination of the interior of a gill pouch.

Pin the first gill pouch open as shown and DRAW.

After the examination of the gill pouch remove the pins and proceed to open up the other gill pouches as indicated by the dotted lines—cuts 1, 2, 3 and 4.

35

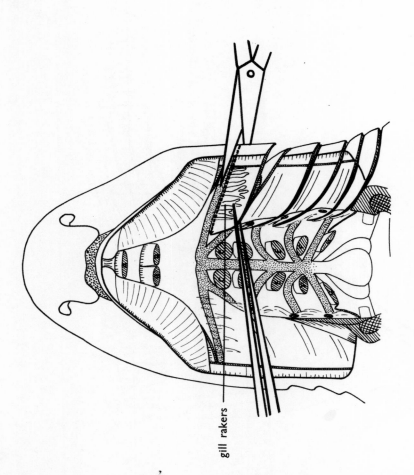

gill rakers

Fig. 35

The first afferent branchial artery is already visible along the
hyoid arch. Clear the connective tissue from it thoroughly and
trim away the gill and gill rakers to the level of the artery.

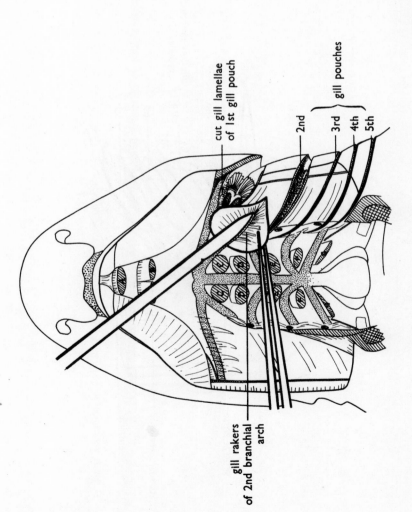

cut gill lamellae
of 1st gill pouch

2nd

3rd
4th
5th } gill pouches

gill rakers
of 2nd branchial
arch

Fig. 36

Follow the second afferent branchial artery out into the gill arch. Use the BACK OF THE SCALPEL for this process rather than the sharp edge of the blade.

NOTE. The gill rakers arise posterior to the artery.

Observe the small holes made where the branches from the artery to the gills are cut.

Trim the gills level with the artery as shown in Fig. 35.

Repeat to expose the third, fourth and fifth afferent branchial arteries.

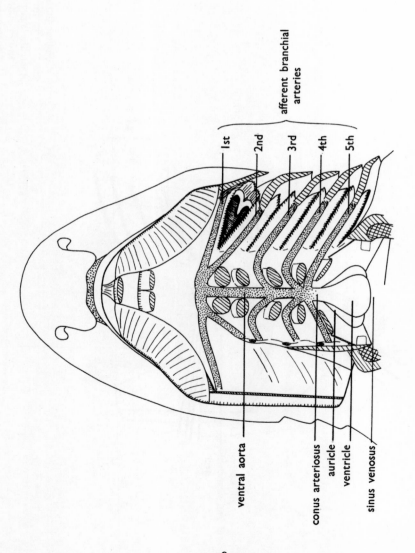

Fig. 37

DRAW the completed dissection of the ventral aorta and afferent branchial arteries.

THE HEART

The ventral view of the heart has already been observed and included in the drawing of Fig. 37. Remove the heart from the pericardial cavity by cutting through the conus arteriosus at its junction with the ventral aorta, and through the sinus venosus.

Fig. 38

Study and DRAW the lateral view of the heart.

Fig. 39

Study and DRAW the dorsal view of the heart.
Make a median dorsal slit through the wall of the sinus venosus and the auricle, inserting one blade of the scissors through the sinu-auricular aperture.

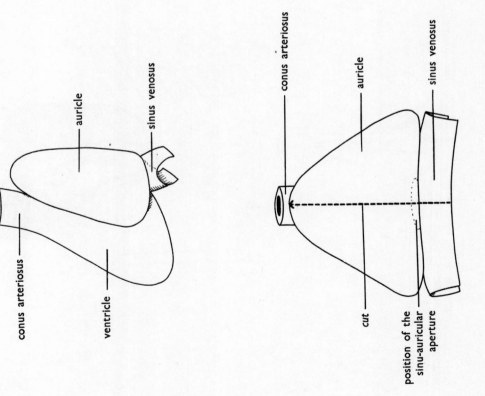

auricle

sinus venosus

conus arteriosus

ventricle

conus arteriosus

auricle

sinus venosus

cut

position of the
sinu-auricular
aperture

THE HEART

Fig. 40

Turn the heart so that the anterior end of the heart is towards you.

Notice the auriculo-ventricular aperture slightly to one side of the midline. Because of this asymmetry the heart must not be cut in two by a single median cut.

Cut through the posterior wall of the ventricle as indicated —cut I.

Follow the cut round to the ventral side of the heart and through the conus arteriosus—cut 2.

Complete the division of the heart—cut 3.

Clean out any blood from the heart.

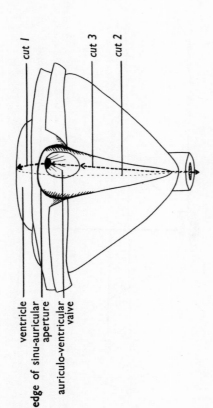

cut I

cut 3
cut 2

ventricle
edge of sinu-auricular aperture
auriculo-ventricular valve

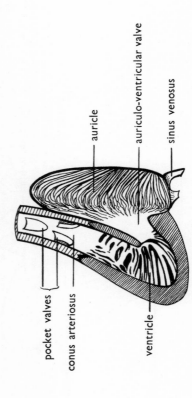

Fig. 41

Study and DRAW the internal structure of the heart.

auricle

auriculo-ventricular valve

sinus venosus

pocket valves
conus arteriosus

ventricle

THE ARTERIAL SYSTEM

(b) THE EFFERENT BRANCHIAL AND EPIBRANCHIAL ARTERIES
AND THE DORSAL AORTA

This part of the arterial system lies dorsal to the pharynx. The appearance of the interior of the buccal cavity and pharynx should be studied during the course of the dissection (Fig. 43). The amount of blood and hence the colour of these arteries varies considerably. They are never as obvious as the afferent branchial arteries.

ONLY ONE SIDE SHOULD BE DISSECTED if the nerves are required later as the branchial branches of the vagus are often cut accidentally.

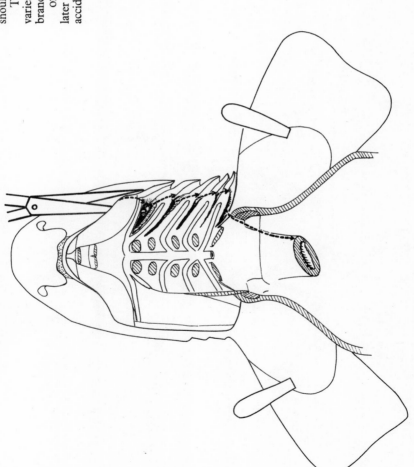

Fig. 42

Insert one blade of the scissors into the mouth and cut through the angle of the jaw. Cut through each branchial arch in turn and down the side of the oesophagus.

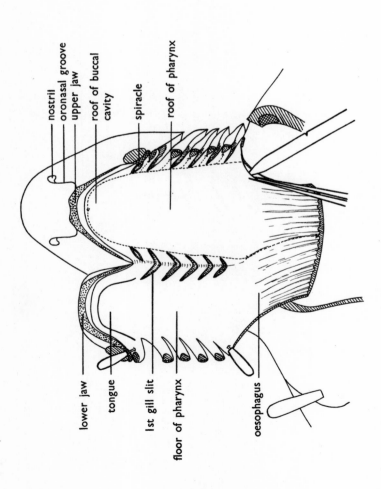

Fig. 43

Pin aside the floor of the buccal cavity and pharynx.
Observe the structures shown and DRAW.

Remove the mucous membrane from the area outlined by
the dotted lines.

N.B. Watch for and be careful not to cut the epibranchial
arteries which lie beneath it.

Slit the mucous membrane along the line of each branchial
arch on the side to be dissected.

nostril
oronasal groove
upper jaw
roof of buccal
cavity
spiracle
roof of pharynx

lower jaw
tongue
1st gill slit
floor of pharynx
oesophagus

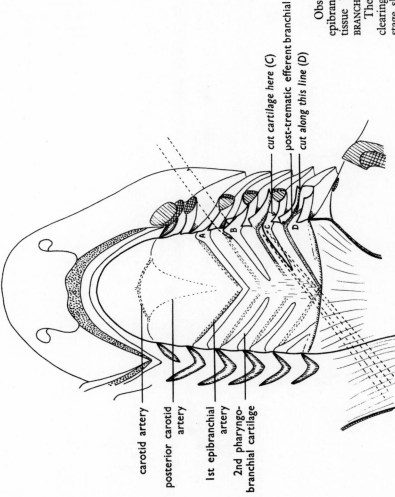

carotid artery

posterior carotid artery

1st epibranchial artery

2nd pharyngo-branchial cartilage

cut cartilage here (C)

post-trematic efferent branchial

cut along this line (D)

Fig. 44

Observe the pharyngo-branchial cartilages and identify the epibranchial arteries. The latter are embedded in connective tissue but SHOULD NOT BE CLEARED UNTIL THE EFFERENT BRANCHIAL VESSELS HAVE BEEN EXPOSED.

The diagram shows successive stages in the process of clearing the post-trematic efferent branchial arteries. Each stage should be repeated on each arch in turn.

A.—The pharyngo-branchial cartilage is in position.

B.—Cut under the head of the pharyngo-branchial cartilage where it joins the cerato-branchial cartilage in the gill arch.

N.B. KEEP THIS CUT AS CLOSE TO THE CARTILAGE AS POSSIBLE.

C.—Observe the blood-vessel underneath the cartilage. Lift the cartilage as indicated. Free it from the epibranchial artery and the connective tissue and muscles of the roof of the pharynx. Cut the cerato-branchial cartilage away.

D.—Cut away the mucous membrane to expose the artery clearly.

NOTE. In the fourth arch the cerato-branchial cartilage should be removed completely so that the connection from the ninth efferent branchial artery is displayed.

Fig. 45

Again successive stages are indicated.

E.—All the arches should appear like this after the completion of D.

F.—Follow the pre-trematic efferent branchial vessel from its junction with the epibranchial artery out into the gill arch. Cut away the mucous membrane so that the vessel is fully exposed.

G.—This is the appearance of the completed dissection of a typical arch.

H.—This shows the appearance of the first arch, which differs from the rest.

Clear the connective tissue from all the vessels indicated by dotted lines in the above figure. To do so, cut slightly to one side of each vessel. The connective tissue is sufficiently elastic to spring aside when so cut.

NOTE. The dorsal aorta is deeper in the anterior region than in the posterior one. It is therefore easier to cut the oesophagus and follow the artery FORWARDS than to attempt to clear the anterior end first. Clear the epibranchial arteries in turn as you come to them. Watch for the subclavian arteries.

Cut away part of the first pharyngo-branchial cartilage from the undissected side.

Trace the dorsal aorta as far back as desired.

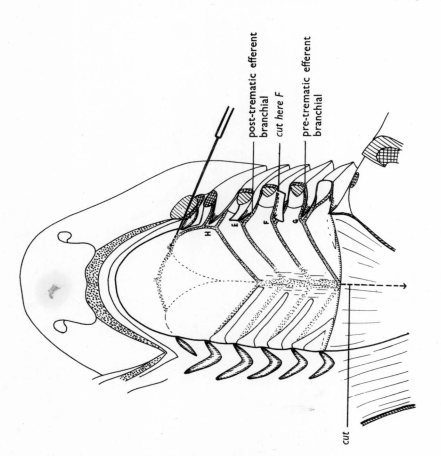

post-trematic efferent
branchial

cut here F

pre-trematic efferent
branchial

cut

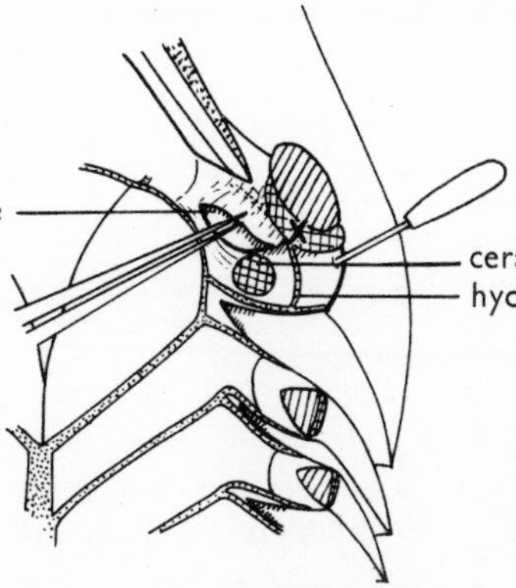

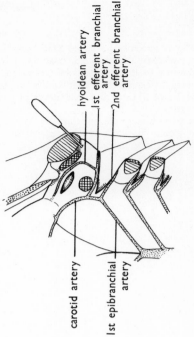

Fig. 47

Use a pin as shown to steady the hyoidean region.

Hold aside the edge of the spiracle and trace the hyoidean artery between it and the cartilages of the angle of the jaw—X.

When the artery has been traced, cut away the edge of the spiracle and the cartilage at X to allow full display of the blood-vessel.

Adjust the position of the pin.

Fig. 48

The completed dissection is shown. It should be drawn in conjunction with Fig. 46.

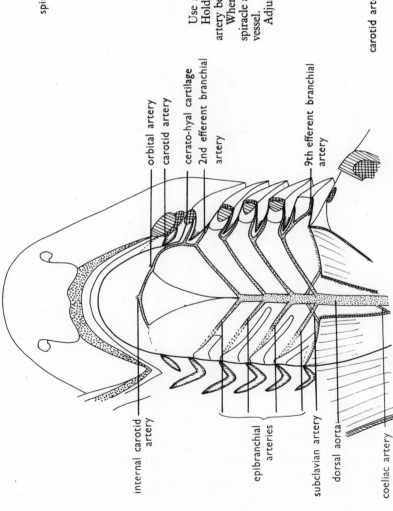

Fig. 46

Examine and DRAW the efferent branchial and epi-branchial arteries.

It is usual to leave the dissection at this stage, but if the hyoidean artery is to be shown, proceed as follows :

Remove the mucous membrane from the area round the spiracle.

Remove the cerato-hyal cartilage, watching for the hyoidean artery which branches from the first efferent branchial artery as shown in Fig. 47.

THE NERVOUS SYSTEM

(a) THE CRANIAL NERVES

If the efferent branchial arteries have been dissected use the opposite side of the dogfish for the dissection of the nerves, particularly the branchial branches of the vagus, see Figs. 59–61, which are liable to have been damaged during the removal of the epibranchial cartilages.

During this dissection drawings should be made at a number of stages in order to show such structures as the extrinsic muscles of the eye and the nerves to these muscles which are removed for full display of the trigeminal and facial nerves.

In order to minimize the labelling on the diagrams the nerves are marked with the name and number only, omitting the words "nerve" or "branch of the —— nerve" as the case may be.

Before starting the dissection, study Fig. 57 carefully.

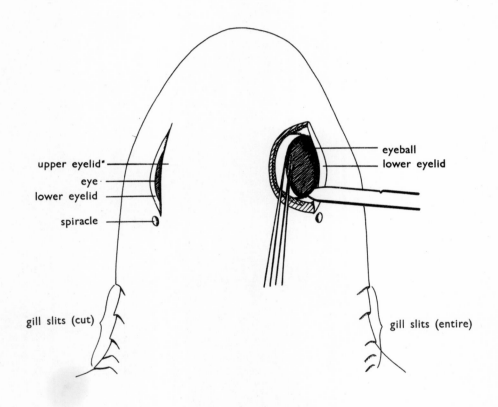

upper eyelid
eye
lower eyelid
spiracle

eyeball
lower eyelid

gill slits (cut)

gill slits (entire)

Fig. 49

Fix the dogfish to the dissecting-board DORSAL SIDE uppermost.

Examine the dorsal surface of the head.

Cut the conjunctiva between the upper eyelid and the eyeball and carve away a portion of the roof of the orbit. This exposes the eyeball as shown.

Cut the conjunctiva between the lower eyelid and the eyeball, holding the eyeball up meanwhile and being CAREFUL NOT TO CUT THE NERVES WHICH CROSS THE FLOOR OF THE ORBIT (see Fig. 51).

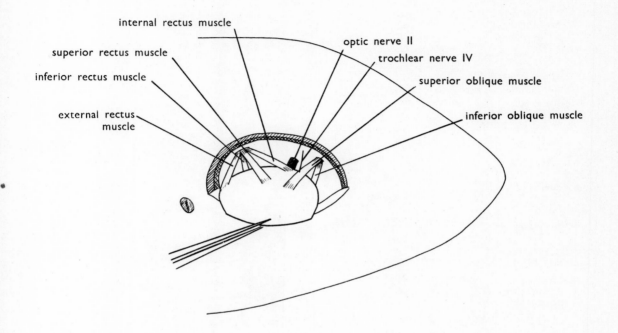

internal rectus muscle

superior rectus muscle

inferior rectus muscle

external rectus muscle

optic nerve II

trochlear nerve IV

superior oblique muscle

inferior oblique muscle

Fig. 50

Remove any loose gelatinous connective tissue from the orbit.
Turn the dogfish and view it from a dorso-lateral direction.
Pull the eyeball towards you. Examine and DRAW the eye-muscles.

Cut each eye-muscle and the optic nerve as close to the eyeball as possible.
Remove the eye.
Cut away the lower eyelid.

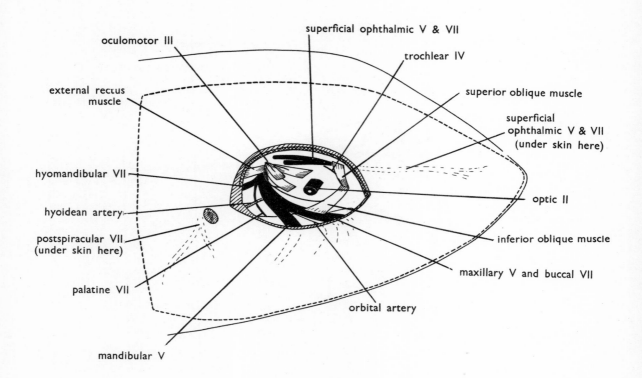

oculomotor III

superficial ophthalmic V & VII

trochlear IV

external rectus muscle

superior oblique muscle

superficial ophthalmic V & VII (under skin here)

hyomandibular VII

hyoidean artery

optic II

postspiracular VII (under skin here)

inferior oblique muscle

palatine VII

maxillary V and buccal VII

orbital artery

mandibular V

Fig. 51

Wash out the orbit.

Turn the superior rectus muscle downwards to show the root of the occulomotor nerve III.

Examine and DRAW the structures visible at this stage.

Cut away the skin from the area outlined by the thick dotted lines, watching for the nerves in the positions marked by the fine dotted lines.

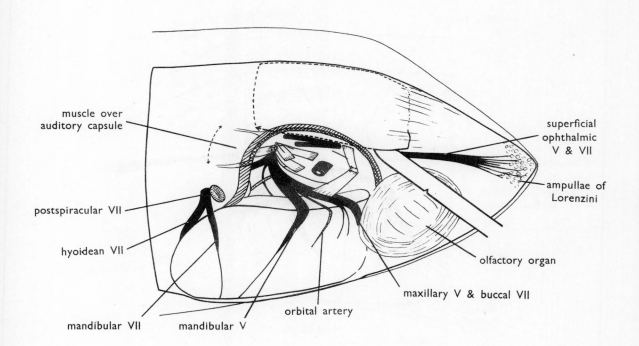

muscle over
auditory capsule

superficial
ophthalmic
V & VII

ampullae of
Lorenzini

postspiracular VII

hyoidean VII

olfactory organ

maxillary V & buccal VII

orbital artery

mandibular VII   mandibular V

Fig. 52

Clear the hyoidean and mandibular branches of the postspiracular part of the facial nerve VII.

Similarly clear the maxillary and mandibular branches of the trigeminal nerve V and the buccal branch of the facial nerve VII.

Note. At this stage the maxillary V and the buccal VII are not readily distinguishable.

Both the mandibular nerves run deep in the muscle of the upper jaw, but can readily be traced if desired by following the lines visible across the muscle.

Clear the anterior portion of the superficial ophthalmic nerves V and VII.

Carve away the roof of the cranium down to the level of the exit of the ophthalmic nerves from the orbit.

N.B. BE CAREFUL NOT TO DAMAGE THE BRAIN.

Remove the rectus and oblique muscles and the third and fourth nerves.

Scrape away the muscle from the dorsal surface of the auditory capsule and cut it back to the line indicated.

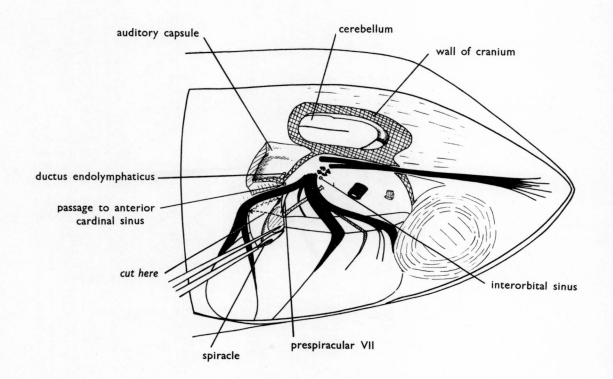

auditory capsule

cerebellum

wall of cranium

ductus endolymphaticus

passage to anterior
cardinal sinus

cut here

interorbital sinus

spiracle

prespiracular VII

Fig. 53

Trace the postspiracular branch of the hyomandibular nerve along its course behind the spiracle. Watch for the prespiracular branch which is very small and variable in its point of origin. It lies close to the posterior wall of the orbit. Cut away the tissue round the spiracle to allow full display of these nerves.

Carve away the dorsal and lateral walls of the auditory capsule carefully. N.B. Cut away only a small piece at a time, working round the membranous labyrinth.

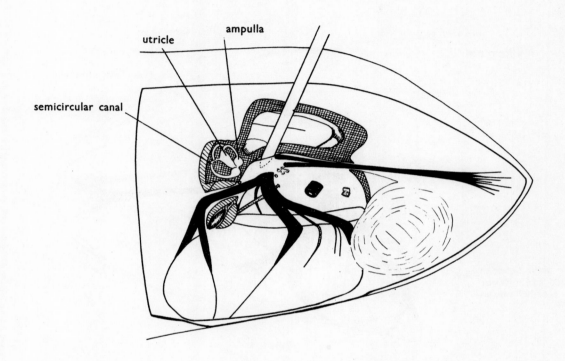

Fig. 54

Observe and DRAW the semicircular canals.

Remove the connective tissue lining the orbit from the cartilage over the area dorsal to the main roots of the trigeminal and facial nerves.

N.B. This may seem unnecessary, but it makes the subsequent removal of the cartilage much easier.

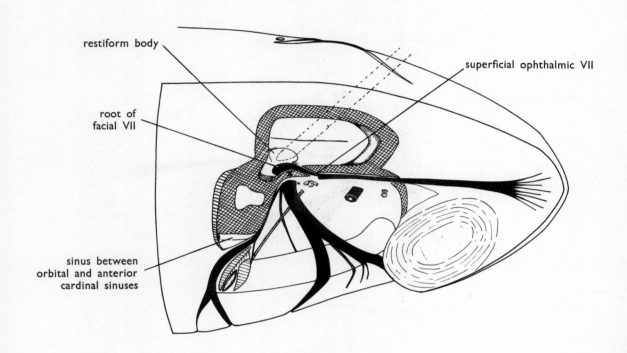

restiform body

superficial ophthalmic VII

root of
facial VII

sinus between
orbital and anterior
cardinal sinuses

Fig. 55

Gradually carve away the cartilage in the region marked X.

NOTE. The membranous labyrinth is destroyed in this process. At intervals hold back the restiform body as indicated so that the root of the facial nerve can be seen and cutting it is avoided.

Trace the superficial ophthalmic branch of the facial nerve through the wall of the cranium.

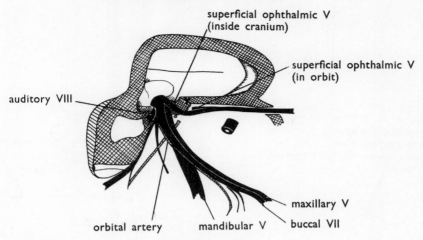

superficial ophthalmic V
(inside cranium)

superficial ophthalmic V
(in orbit)

auditory VIII

maxillary V

orbital artery   mandibular V   buccal VII

Fig. 56

Clear the root of the facial nerve. Remove the connective tissue of the lining of the orbit from the surface of the nerves. The buccal branch of the facial nerve can then be identified crossing the trigeminal nerve as shown. Use a seeker to separate these nerves and observe the branching of both buccal and maxillary nerves to serve the upper jaw.

Observe and clear the auditory nerve.

Loosen the superficial ophthalmic branch of the facial nerve from the cranial wall as shown.

Carve away the cartilage at Y to expose the superficial ophthalmic branch of the trigeminal nerve.

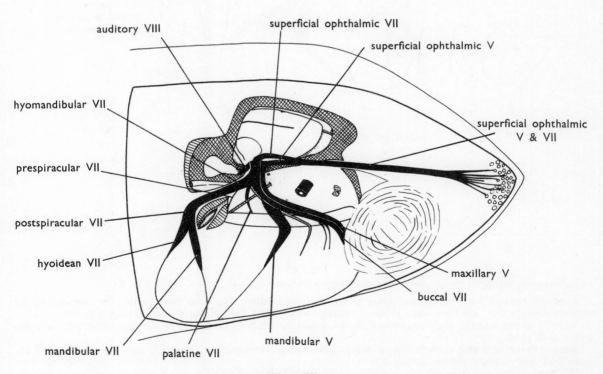

auditory VIII   superficial ophthalmic VII

superficial ophthalmic V

hyomandibular VII

superficial ophthalmic
V & VII

prespiracular VII

postspiracular VII

hyoidean VII

maxillary V

buccal VII

mandibular VII   palatine VII   mandibular V

Fig. 57

Study and DRAW the completed dissection of the fifth and seventh cranial nerves.

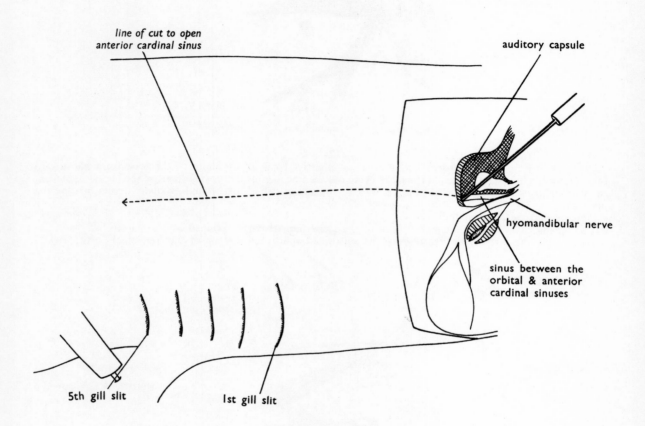

Fig. 58

Before proceeding to the dissection of the ninth and tenth cranial nerves, study Fig. 61.

Find the passage from the orbital sinus to the anterior cardinal sinus. It runs against the cartilage of the auditory capsule and will have been exposed during the previous part of the dissection—see Fig. 55.

Insert a seeker into the anterior cardinal sinus. Open the sinus by cutting along the line indicated, using the seeker as a guide.

NOTE. If the fifth and seventh cranial nerves have not previously been dissected, start the dissection of the ninth and tenth cranial nerves as follows :

(*a*) Remove the skin from the region immediately dorsal to the spiracle, i.e. that covering the auditory capsule.

(*b*) Remove the muscle from the dorsal and lateral surfaces of the auditory capsule. Observe the opening of the cardinal sinus and continue as above.

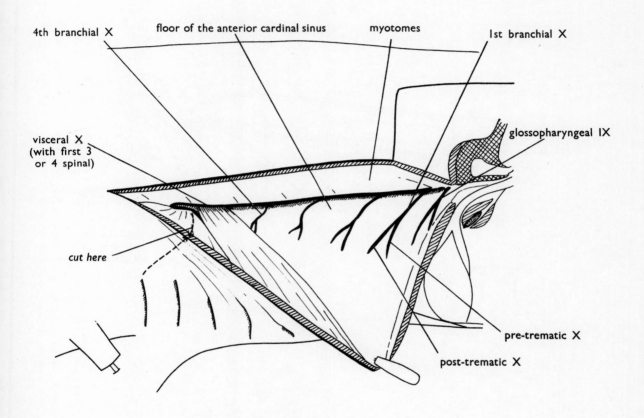

4th branchial X

floor of the anterior cardinal sinus

myotomes

1st branchial X

visceral X
(with first 3
or 4 spinal)

glossopharyngeal IX

cut here

pre-trematic X

post-trematic X

Fig. 59

Open the anterior cardinal sinus. Pin back the lateral wall. Observe the structures labelled in the diagram. Cut through the last gill slit and cut through the muscle of the pectoral girdle along a line to meet this slit.

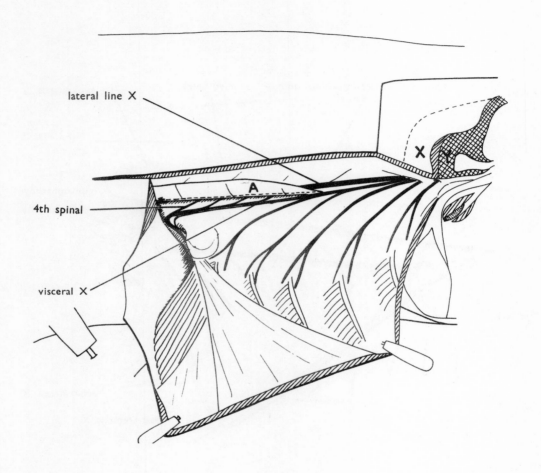

lateral line X

4th spinal

visceral X

Fig. 60

Pin as shown above.

Carefully clear the connective tissue from the glossopharyngeal nerve and from the branchial branches of the vagus.

Observe the visceral branch of the vagus and the spinal nerves. They are bound together as shown and must be carefully separated.

Clean away the connective tissue from the median wall of the cardinal sinus and observe the root of the lateral line branch of the vagus.

Trace this lateral line nerve behind the muscle marked A. Cut A away as completely as possible.

Carve away the muscle at X and the cartilage at Y to trace the roots of the glossopharyngeal and vagus nerves through the floor of the auditory capsule to the brain.

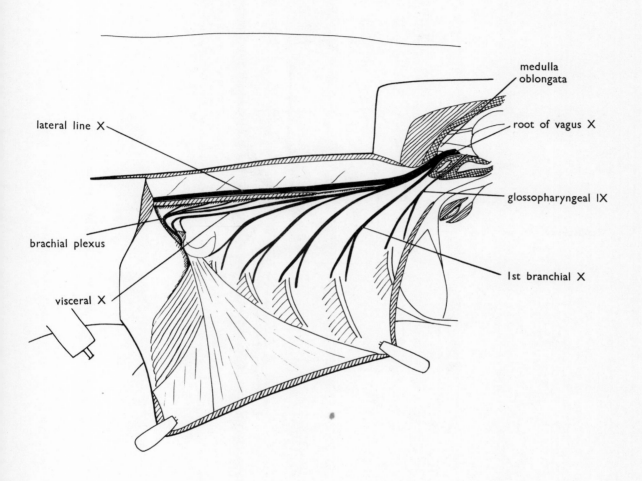

medulla
oblongata

root of vagus X

lateral line X

glossopharyngeal IX

brachial plexus

1st branchial X

visceral X

Fig. 61

Observe and DRAW the nerves shown.
NOTICE ESPECIALLY THE SEPARATION OF THE VISCERAL BRANCH OF THE VAGUS FROM THE BRACHIAL PLEXUS.

(b) THE BRAIN

When the dissection of the cranial nerves has been completed, the brain should be removed from the cranium and studied separately.

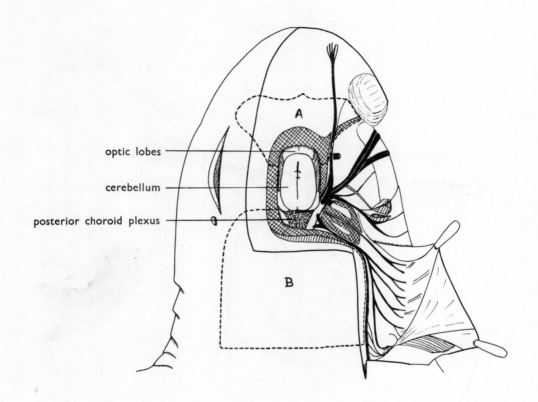

optic lobes

cerebellum

posterior choroid plexus

Fig. 62

The completed dissection of the cranial nerves is seen on the right of the diagram, but the left side is shown undissected.

Carve away the skin, muscle and cartilage from the areas marked A and B. Keep the scalpel horizontal while making these cuts in order to avoid damaging the brain.

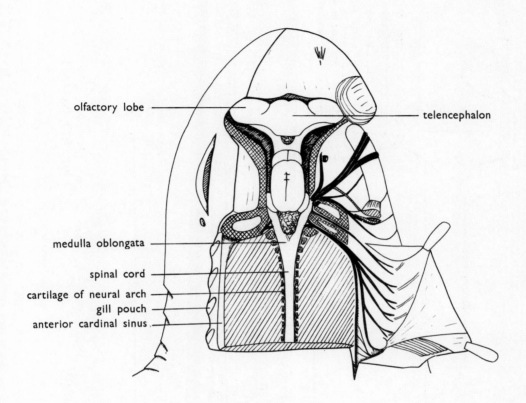

olfactory lobe

telencephalon

medulla oblongata

spinal cord

cartilage of neural arch

gill pouch

anterior cardinal sinus

Fig. 63

Observe the brain in position in the cranium.

Cut through the spinal cord a short distance behind the medulla oblongata. Cut through each of the cranial nerves in turn, working forwards and lifting the brain from the cranium as you proceed.

NOTE. CUT THE NERVES AS CLOSE TO THE CRANIUM AS POSSIBLE so that the roots can be identified later. Cut between the olfactory lobe and the olfactory organ with a scalpel, but cut the other nerves with scissors.

THE NERVOUS SYSTEM

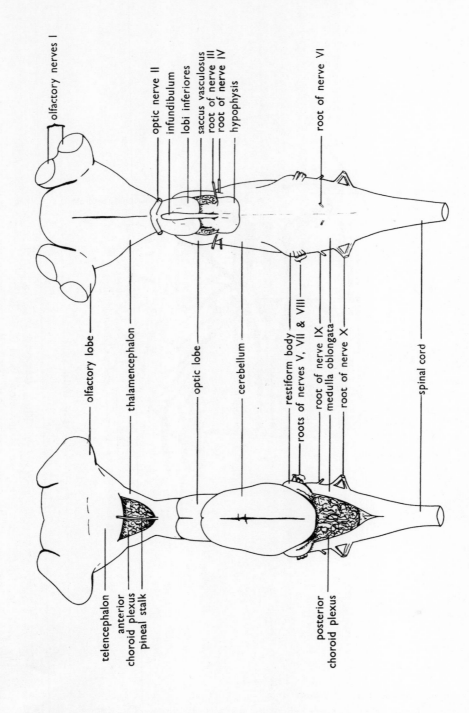

olfactory nerves I

optic nerve II
infundibulum
lobi inferiores
saccus vasculosus
root of nerve III
root of nerve IV
hypophysis

root of nerve VI

olfactory lobe

thalamencephalon

optic lobe

cerebellum

restiform body
roots of nerves V, VII & VIII
root of nerve IX
medulla oblongata
root of nerve X

spinal cord

telencephalon
anterior
choroid plexus
pineal stalk

posterior
choroid plexus

Fig. 64a (dorsal)

Fig. 64b (ventral)

60

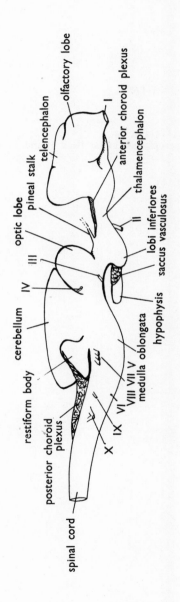

Fig. 64c (lateral)

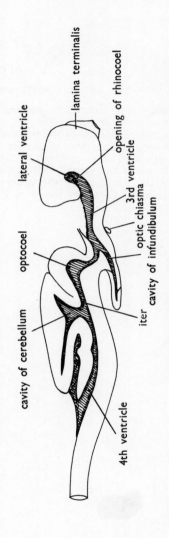

Fig. 64d (half)

Figs. 64a–64d

Study and DRAW draw dorsal, ventral and lateral views of the brain.
Cut the brain through the median sagittal plane. Study and DRAW one-half of the brain, noticing the
position of the ventricles.

APPENDIX

THE COMPLETE DISSECTION OF THE ALIMENTARY CANAL

To display the alimentary canal completely, proceed as follows :

(1) Open the body cavity—see Figs. 1-5.

(2) Carve away the ventral portion of the pectoral girdle—see Figs. 13 and 24.

(3) Cut through the angle of the jaw, gill arches and side of the oesophagus as far back as the pericardio-peritoneal septum on one side only—see Fig. 42.

(4) Cut transversely across the ventral wall of the oesophagus.

(5) Pin the floor of the buccal cavity and pharynx aside—see Fig. 43.

(6) Display the abdominal viscera as shown in Figs. 6-8.

KU-626-986

my **revisi⏻n** notes

OCR AS/A-level History

RUSSIA
1894–1941

Andrew Holland

Series Editor
Nick Fellows

HODDER
EDUCATION
AN HACHETTE UK COMPANY

Every effort has been made to trace all copyright holders, but if any have been inadvertently overlooked, the Publishers will be pleased to make the necessary arrangements at the first opportunity.

Although every effort has been made to ensure that website addresses are correct at time of going to press, Hodder Education cannot be held responsible for the content of any website mentioned in this book. It is sometimes possible to find a relocated web page by typing in the address of the home page for a website in the URL window of your browser.

Hachette UK's policy is to use papers that are natural, renewable and recyclable products and made from wood grown in well-managed forests and other controlled sources. The logging and manufacturing processes are expected to conform to the environmental regulations of the country of origin.

Orders: please contact Hachette UK Distribution, Hely Hutchinson Centre, Milton Road, Didcot, Oxfordshire, OX11 7HH. Telephone: +44 (0)1235 827827. Email education@hachette.co.uk Lines are open from 9 a.m. to 5 p.m., Monday to Friday. You can also order through our website: www.hoddereducation.co.uk

ISBN: 978 1 4718 7600 4

© Andy Holland 2017

First published in 2017 by

Hodder Education

An Hachette UK Company

Carmelite House

50 Victoria Embankment

London EC4Y 0DZ

www.hoddereducation.co.uk

Impression number 10 9 8 7 6 5

Year   2022

All rights reserved. Apart from any use permitted under UK copyright law, no part of this publication may be reproduced or transmitted in any form or by any means, electronic or mechanical, including photocopying and recording, or held within any information storage and retrieval system, without permission in writing from the publisher or under licence from the Copyright Licensing Agency Limited. Further details of such licences (for reprographic reproduction) may be obtained from the Copyright Licensing Agency Limited, www.cla.co.uk.
Cover photo © Aleksandr Kurganov / Alamy Stock Photo
Illustrations by Integra
Typeset by Integra Software Services Pvt. Ltd., Pondicherry, India
Printed and bound by CPI Group (UK) Ltd, Croydon CR0 4YY

A catalogue record for this title is available from the British Library.

My Revision Planner

4 The rule of Stalin

REVISED

Introduction

Russia: 1894–1941

The specification lists the content under four key topics.
- Key Topic 1 – The rule of Tsar Nicholas II
- Key Topic 2 – The 1917 Revolutions
- Key Topic 3 – The Civil War and Lenin
- Key Topic 4 – The rule of Stalin

Although each period of study is set out in chronological sections in the specification, an exam question may arise from one or more of these sections.

AS-Level

The AS examination which you may be taking includes all the content.

You are required to answer:
- Section A: ONE. question from a choice of TWO. They are traditional essays and will require you to use your knowledge to explain, analyse and assess key features of the period studied and then reach a judgement about the issue in the question. The question is worth 30 marks.
- Section B: ONE interpretation question. The specification names the two Key Topics from which the interpretation will be drawn. Questions will require candidates to evaluate the strengths and limitations of a given historical interpretation, in the form of either one or two sentences, by applying their own knowledge and awareness of the debate to the given interpretation. The question is worth 20 marks.

The exam lasts one and a half hours, and you are advised to spend slightly more time on Section A.

At AS-Level, Unit 2 will be worth a total of 50 marks and 50 per cent of the AS examination.

A-Level

The A-Level examination at the end of the course includes all the content.

You are required to answer ONE question with TWO parts from a choice of TWO questions:
- Each question will have TWO parts. Question (a) will be a short essay in which you are asked to analyse two issues and reach a judgement as to which is the more important or significant. Question (b) is a traditional period study essay and will require you to use your knowledge to explain, analyse and assess key features of the period studied and then reach a judgement about the issue in the question.
- The short essay is worth 10 marks and the traditional essay is worth 20 marks.
- The two parts of each question will be drawn from different parts of the specification.

The exam lasts for one hour. You should spend about 20 minutes on Question (a) and 40 minutes on Question (b).

At A-Level, Unit 2 will be worth a total of 30 marks and 15 per cent of the A-Level examination.

In both the AS and A-Level examinations you are being tested on the ability to:
- use relevant historical information
- use the skill of analysing factors and reaching a judgement.

In the AS examination you are also being tested on your ability to analyse and evaluate the different ways in which aspects of the past have been interpreted.

How to use this book

This book has been designed to help you develop the knowledge and skills necessary to succeed in the examination.
- The book is divided into four sections – one for each section of the AS and A-Level specifications.
- Each section is made up of a series of topics organised into double page spreads.

- On the left-hand page you will find a summary of the key content you will need to learn.
- Words in bold in the key content are defined in the glossary (see pages 88–90).
- On the right-hand page you will find exam-focused activities.

Together, these two strands of the book will provide you with the knowledge and skills essential for examination success.

▼ **Key historical content**

▼ **Exam-focused activities**

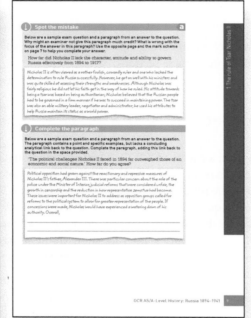

Examination activities

There are three levels of exam-focused activities:

- Band 1 activities are designed to develop the foundation skills needed to pass the exam. These have a blue heading and this symbol.
- Band 2 activities are designed to build on the skills developed in Band 1 activities and to help you to achieve a C grade. These have an orange heading and this symbol.
- Band 3 activities are designed to enable you to access the highest grades. These have a puple heading and this symbol.

Some of the activities have answers or suggested answers on pages 94-96. These have the following symbol to indicate this.

Each section ends with exam-style questions and sample answers with commentary. This will give you guidance on what is expected to achieve the top grade.

You can also keep track of your revision by ticking off each topic heading in the book, or by ticking the checklist on the contents page. Tick each box when you have:

- revised and understood a topic
- completed the activities.

Mark schemes

For some of the activities in the book it will be useful to refer to the mark schemes for this paper. Below are abbreviated forms.

AS-Level

Level	Essay	Interpretation
5	Mostly focused, supported answer with good analysis and evaluation to reach a supported judgement. [25–30]	Very good analysis of the interpretation, aware of the debate and uses detailed knowledge to evaluate the strengths and limitations. [17–20]
4	Some focus with support, analysis with limited evaluation and judgement. [19–24]	Good analysis of the interpretation, some awareness of the debate and uses knowledge to evaluate the strengths and limitations. [13–16]
3	Partial focus on the question, with some knowledge and analysis, but little or no judgement. [13–18]	Partial analysis of the interpretation, some knowledge and awareness of the debate. May be limited in treatment of strength or limitations. [9–12]
2	Focus is descriptive and may be more on the topic than the question. Any analysis may be implied. [7–12]	Limited analysis, may describe the interpretation and the debate. Any evaluation is implied or superficial. [5–8]
1	Focus on the topic and attempts at analysis will be little more than assertion. [1–6]	Focused more on the topic than the given interpretation. Knowledge is general and evaluation is asserted. [1–4]

A-Level

Level	Short-answer essay	Essay
6	Analyses and evaluates both factors with detailed knowledge to reach a developed judgement. [9–10]	Well-focused, supported answer with very good analysis and developed evaluation to reach a supported and sustained judgement. [17–20]
5	Analyses and evaluates both factors with some knowledge to reach a developed judgement. [7–8]	Mostly focused, supported answer with good analysis and evaluation to reach a supported judgement. [13–16]
4	Some analysis and evaluation of both factors, with some support and judgement. [5–6]	Some focus with support, analysis with limited evaluation and judgement. [10–12]
3	Partial analysis and evaluation with some knowledge to reach a basic judgement. [3–4]	Partial focus on the question, with some knowledge and analysis, but little or no judgement. [7–9]
2	Limited analysis and knowledge, with a simple judgement. [2]	Focus is descriptive and may be more on the topic than the question. Any analysis may be implied. [4–6]
1	General analysis and knowledge with assertion. [1]	Focus on the topic and attempts at analysis will be little more than assertion. [1–3]

1 The rule of Tsar Nicholas II

The character, attitude and abilities of Nicholas II

REVISED

Character

Nicholas II is often viewed by historians, as he was by many of his contemporaries, as weak-willed, poorly educated, lacking confidence, a bad judge of people and devious. He is said to have 'lacked that taste for power which is vital for an autocrat.' He could also be very obstinate, as was displayed when he took charge of the Russian military during the First World War. However, Nicholas could also be gentle, kind and benevolent, prompting one historian to state that his 'character may be said to be essentially feminine.'

Attitude

The attitude of Nicholas towards governing was based on a faith in God, a sense of duty and a rigid belief in autocracy. The tsar, like his forebears, believed that religion and tsarism were inextricably linked. In the Fundamental Laws of 1906 it was stated that: 'The All Russian Emperor possesses the supreme autocratic power. Not only fear and conscience, but God himself, commands obedience to his authority.' Furthermore, Nicholas stated that it was his duty to 'uphold the principle of autocracy as firmly and as unflinchingly as did my ever lamented father.' Thus, adherence to the dogma of autocracy would also have meant that he prioritised maintenance of the Romanov dynasty.

Abilities

Given the character of Nicholas and his attitude towards tsarism it is difficult to see that he had any kind of ability to rule successfully. Indeed, his weaknesses as ruler are often cited as the main reason for the downfall of the Romanov dynasty and the spiralling of Russia into revolution and a state of civil war. However, Nicholas did show an ability to instigate reforms (such as the establishment of the Dumas) and to enforce them with a firm hand. It is sometimes the latter ability that has led to him being viewed as obstinate.

Problems of Russia in 1894

Political

Opposition had grown against the reactionary and repressive measures of Alexander III. Of particular concern were:

- the centralised control of the police under the Minister of Interior
- the replacement of elected Justices of the Peace with 'Land Captains'
- a rise in censorship
- the tighter control of the zemstva (provincial governments) and a reduction of peasant representation in these organisations.

In general, opposition groups called for reforms to the political system to allow for greater representation of the people.

Economic

The main economic problems were:
- a lack of productivity compared with international rivals. Up to 1894 industrialisation had resulted in an average annual economic growth rate of 8 per cent, but much of this was achieved through small-scale enterprise.
- a lack of free enterprise. The tsar and his ministers directed production by controlling the armaments industry and the railways – the main consumers of industrial products.
- a reliance on foreign investment.
- rising exports of grain, which had contributed to the terrible famine of 1891.
- Agriculture was backward, with many peasants still using wooden ploughs that limited productivity.

Social

Social issues arose both in the countryside and towns.
- Despite the formation of a Peasants' Land Bank (1883) and the abolition of the peasant poll tax (1886), peasants were still aggrieved about their living standards. The redistribution of land had resulted in a reduction in the size of plots and the mir continued to be a barrier to innovation.
- The 1891 famine resulted in the deaths of over 350,000 people; its impact was long-lasting.
- Industrialisation led to urbanisation and associated public health problems such as poor housing, lack of sanitation and inadequate water supplies. The result was the spread of diseases, especially cholera.

Spot the mistake ⓐ

Below are a sample exam question and a paragraph from an answer to the question. Why might an examiner not give this paragraph much credit? What is wrong with the focus of the answer in this paragraph? Use the opposite page and the mark scheme on page 7 to help you complete your answer.

How far did Nicholas II lack the character, attitude and ability to govern Russia effectively from 1894 to 1917?

Nicholas II is often viewed as a rather foolish, cowardly ruler and one who lacked the determination to rule Russia successfully. However, he got on well with his ministers and was quite skilled at assessing their strengths and weaknesses. Although Nicholas was fairly religious he did not let his faith get in the way of how he ruled. His attitude towards being a tsar was based on being authoritarian; Nicholas believed that the Russian people had to be governed in a firm manner if he was to succeed in maintaining power. The tsar was also an able military leader, negotiator and administrator; he used his attributes to help Russia maintain its status as a world power.

 Complete the paragraph

Below are a sample exam question and a paragraph from an answer to the question. The paragraph contains a point and specific examples, but lacks a concluding analytical link back to the question. Complete the paragraph, adding this link back to the question in the space provided.

'The political challenges Nicholas II faced in 1894 far outweighed those of an economic and social nature.' How far do you agree?

Political opposition had grown against the reactionary and repressive measures of Nicholas II's father, Alexander III. There was particular concern about the role of the police under the Minister of Interior, judicial reforms that were considered unfair, the growth in censorship and the reduction in how representative zemstva had become. These issues were important for Nicholas II to address as opposition groups called for reforms to the political system to allow for greater representation of the people. If concessions were made, Nicholas would have experienced a watering down of his authority. Overall,

_____

_____

Opposition to Nicholas II

Opposition to the tsar arose partly in the form of political groups which had started to form, albeit illegally, during the rule of Alexander III. They were tolerated as long as they acted within the bounds of the law. In 1905 Nicholas II made political parties legal in the hope that they would continue to act responsibly. The groups that arose are usually categorised as Liberals, Populists and Marxists.

Liberals

By 1894 liberal 'Westernisers' (as opposed to Slavophiles) continued to demand that Russia should be governed in a similar way to Western European democracies such as Britain. Liberal ideas were supported by the emergence of the *zemstva* and the mid-1890s revival of the concept of a *zemstvo* union. In 1904 Pyotr Struve founded the Union of Liberation, which demanded greater freedoms and justice for all Russians. In particular, the Union wanted fairer and more land distribution for peasants, a representative Constituent Assembly, and improved conditions for industrial workers.

Kadets and Octobrists

After the so-called revolution of 1905, the clamour for a constitutional monarchy gathered pace with the formation of the Constitutional Democrats (Kadets). Led by Paul Milyukov, this was the intellectual arm of the liberal movement, and went on to play a very important role as opposition within the first *Duma*. A more moderate liberal group also emerged at this time, called the Octobrists. These were individuals, such as Alexander Guchkov and Mikhail Rodzianko, who displayed loyalty to the tsar, but who wanted changes to the system of government. The Octobrists, in particular, supported Nicholas II's October Manifesto (see page 18) and were therefore much maligned by more revolutionary organisations.

Populists

The Populists were revolutionaries, operating in the 1870s, who believed that agricultural communes and co-operative workshops would provide a base for the Russian economy to develop without resorting to capitalism. The Socialist Revolutionaries (SRs) of the early twentieth century emerged from the Populist movement.

The Socialist Revolutionaries (SRs)

The Socialist Revolutionaries continued to focus on improving the living conditions of most disadvantaged people in society, including the growing urban proletariat. The Socialist Revolutionary Party was formed in 1901, led by the intellectual Victor Chernov. By 1905 the group had split into the more radical left-wing SRs and the moderate right-wing SRs. The left employed direct action; from 1901 to 1905 they were responsible for about 2,000 political killings, including those of Grand Duke Sergei and Vyacheslav Plehve. The right worked with other parties and groups, gathering support and momentum after the 1905 revolution (see page 18). The right appealed to peasants, whereas the left focused on the plight of industrial workers. Despite the divisions, the SRs had the most support and were the biggest threat to tsarist rule before the October 1917 revolution.

Marxists

Another revolutionary group, the Social Democrats (SDs), emerged at the same time as the SRs. The SDs based their ideology on the writings of Karl Marx, believing that the proletariat could be 'educated' to overthrow Russian autocracy by way of a revolution.

The Social Democrats (SDs)

In 1898 the All-Russian Social Democratic Workers' Party was founded in Minsk. The group was influenced by an interpretation of Karl Marx's work made by George Plekhanov, who emphasised the need to encourage working-class consciousness. However, since few workers had the time or inclination to engage with Marxist theory, some SD supporters (labelled Mensheviks) focused on improving pay and lowering working hours. By 1903 there were signs of division between the Mensheviks and an opposing faction, the Bolsheviks. The latter argued that workers were capable of being sufficiently politically educated to create a revolution.

Delete as applicable

Below are a sample exam question and a paragraph from an answer to the question. Read the paragraph and decide which of the possible options (in bold) is most appropriate. Delete the least appropriate options and complete the paragraph by justifying your selection.

How successful was opposition to Nicholas II in achieving its aims in the period from 1894 to 1917?

The opposition to Nicholas II came in the form of **a couple/a number/hundreds** of groups who had **similar/partly different/totally different** aims. The main aim of the Liberals was to move towards a constitutional monarchy. The establishment of the Dumas went some way to satisfying their wants although Nicholas II retained his autocratic authority through the Fundamental Laws of 1906. The Populists were less successful as their campaigning for improvements in better working and living conditions for peasants and workers was **partly/mostly/totally** ineffectual. However, through the assassination of key political figures such as Grand Duke Sergei they did create fear within the Russian hierarchy. Finally, the Marxists, in the **short-term/long-term**, were the least successful in achieving their aims; their wish for a revolution and the **partial/complete** overthrow of the tsar was not met until 1917.

_____

_____

Spider diagram

Read the question and complete the spider diagram to identify the degree of threat posed by various opposition groups to Nicholas II. Add a sentence of explanation to each point on the diagram. Then prioritise the degree of threat posed by each group by adding numbers to each oval box – with 1 as identifying the most threatening group and 6 as the least threatening.

'The opposition group that posed the greatest threat to the authority of Nicholas II was the Populists.' How far do you agree?

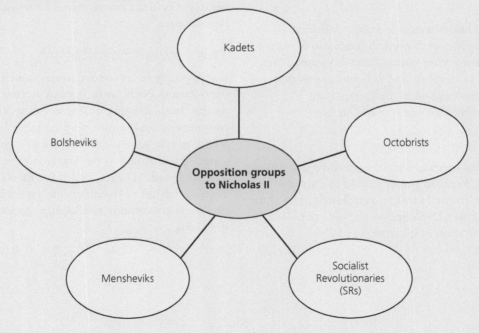

The position of national minorities, 1894 to 1917

In the middle of the nineteenth century the Russian Empire consisted of Great Russia and 'national minorities' (that is, those who did not originate from the Russian peoples). The main national minority groups were from Poland, Finland, the Caucasus and Central Asia and the Baltic Provinces (Estonia, Latvia and Lithuania). Russian Jews stand out as a unique national minority in that their geographical location was one that was artificially created (**The Pale**) and crossed the boundaries of other groups.

Not all national minorities opposed the ruling elites during Nicholas II's rule. In general, the Finnish, Baltic German and Christian Armenian populations remained fairly loyal, whereas the Polish, Ukranian and Tartar populations were a constant thorn in the side of Nicholas II.

The main objective of the 'unco-operative' national minorities was to gain autonomy or even to break away from central Russian rule and gain independence. Subsequently, many of the minorities were made subject to a policy of **Russification** in order to keep them in check.

Russification was the process whereby non-Russian regions were drawn more securely into the framework of the empire. This involved administrative integration and the transmission of Russian language, religion and culture to the peoples of National minorities. Such 'social Russification' was linked to economic integration especially developments telecommunications and transport. Russification started with the Polish Revolt of 1863 and was continued by Lenin, Stalin and Khrushchev mainly through constitutional changes and repression.

Poland

As a result of industrialisation in Poland, a distinct proletariat emerged that showed an interest in Marxism. Also of prominence were nationalists who formed the National Democrats group. Polish politicians elected from these parties went on to make important contributions to the first and second *Dumas*.

Ukraine

Although nationalism was not the same force as it was in Poland, many Ukrainian people looked to assert and strengthen their cultural identity, as reflected in literature and the arts in general. In response the tsar continued the policy of Russification in Ukraine.

The Caucasus

Those living in the regions of Russia known as The Caucasus were divided along religious lines. Some regions, such as Armenia, were almost exclusively Christian while others, such as Chechnya, had a majority Muslim population. These divisions, coupled with the high level of illiteracy in the region, made Russification relatively easy. Nevertheless, Populist movements (such as the Dashnaks and the Georgian Mensheviks) emerged to oppose Nicholas II's repressive measures.

Finland

The appointment by Nicholas II of Nikolai Bobrikov as Governor General marked a change in fortune for the people of Finland. Under Bobrikov, Finland was fully integrated into the Russian Empire and Russified. This provoked much opposition and, as a result, in 1905 Finland was given full autonomy. But this was quickly reneged on by Stolypin in the same year.

Latvia, Lithuania and Estonia

At the start of the period, the Baltic Provinces were strongly influenced by its links with Germany and its earlier rulers. The states were relatively stable and prosperous, especially given the abundant supplies of raw materials that were essential to a range of industrial activities. Riga (in Latvia), became a very important commercial and business centre for Russia. As the Russian economic influence increased in the area, Russification followed naturally. But as German influence waned by the end of the century there was a rise in nationalism among native Estonians, Latvians and Lithuanians.

The Jewish population

Jewish people never seemed to pose much direct opposition to Nicholas II. It was a perceived threat that resulted in them being treated so badly. Nicholas II continued the antisemitic position taken by his father. Jewish people were accused of being 'revolutionaries' as some were affiliated to the SDs (and there was indeed a separate Jewish SD Party called the *Bund*). Despite Nicholas' dislike of Jewish people, he made some important concessions by allowing them to sit on the *Duma*.

Support or challenge?

Below is a sample exam question which asks how far you agree with a specific statement. Below this is a series of general statements that are relevant to the question. Using your own knowledge and the information on the opposite page, decide whether these statements support or challenge the statement in the question.

'Of all the national minorities, the Polish people posed the greatest threat to the stability of the Russian Empire from 1894 to 1917?' How far do you agree?

	Support	Challenge
The threat from the Poles grew significantly during the period in question		
The threat from the Ukrainians was never great		
The threat from the Caucasians was unimportant compared to that from the Ukrainians		
The threat from the Finns was greater than that from the Poles		
The threat from the peoples of the Baltic Provinces fluctuated during the period		
There were times when the threat from Jewish people was considerable		

Simple essay style

Below is a sample exam question. Use your own knowledge and the information on the opposite page to produce a plan for this question. Choose four general points, and provide three pieces of specific information to support each general point.

Once you have planned your essay, write the introduction and conclusion for the essay. The introduction should list the points to be discussed in the essay. The conclusion should summarise the key points and justify which point was the most important.

'Russification was a complete failure in the period from 1894 to 1917' How far do you agree?

The role of individuals: Pobedonostsev and Witte

Konstantin Pobedonostsev (1827–1907) was a significant figure during the rule of Nicholas II: in his role as Chief Procurator of the Holy Synod, he influenced the tsar to adhere to conservatism. **Sergei Witte** (1849–1915) was another individual who left his mark on tsarist policy: as Minister of Finance he promoted a liberal approach to the development of the economy. However, like Pobedonostsev, he held a conservative view on Russian politics.

Pobedonostsev's background

Pobedonostev's early career unfolded as follows:

- In 1841 he enrolled at the St Petersburg School of Jurisprudence.
- He started teaching at Moscow State University in 1860.
- In 1865 he became tutor to Alexander II's sons, Nicholas and Alexander.
- In 1868 he was appointed as a Senator.
- By 1873 he showed signs of being more reactionary, condemning the judicial system.

Ideology

Pobedonostsev was a conservative and reactionary for much of his adult life. He was an advocate of autocracy and an enemy of liberal democracy. The clamour for greater freedom was said, by Pobedonostsev, to be influenced by 'the dangerous delusions of **nihilistic** youth'. Devoutly religious, he venerated the Russian Orthodox Church. Pobedonostov also held antisemitic views and was behind many of the pogroms, or attacks on Jewish people, that took place in this period. However, his influence faded during the reign of Nicholas II until his death in 1907.

Achievements

- Pobedonostsev helped prepare judicial reforms for the tsar in 1864.
- He became an adviser and writer on Russian law; from 1868 to 1880 he published the three volumes of 'A Course of Civil Law'.
- He was a major influence on Alexander III's policymaking and manifesto.
- He became the Chief Procurator of the Holy Synod in 1880; this post allowed him to advise the tsar on religious matters and influence the Church and educational and social policies.

Witte's background

Witte's early career unfolded as follows:

- In 1891 he became Minister for Transport and Minister for Finance in 1892.
- He was dismissed from his post in 1903, having been blamed for a worsening economy.
- In 1905 he was appointed as President of the Council of Ministers and helped negotiate peace with Japan, but was again dismissed from his post in 1906.

Ideology

Witte was the first government minister to show total commitment to industrialisation so that Russia could compete with other industrialised nations and improve its military capability (in 1914, he argued that Russia was not ready for war). The main strands of his plan were:

- the resurrection of **Reutern**'s idea of encouraging foreign experts to come to Russia
- a return to taking out foreign loans (negotiated in 1906), raising taxes and interest rates to boost available capital for investment in industry.

Achievements

In 1897 the **rouble** was placed on the **gold standard**. Witte insisted that most state investment (and control) focus on heavy industry and the railways.

The effect of this was a 'Great Spurt' in economic activity:

- Coal production doubled and that of iron and steel increased sevenfold.
- New technologies were introduced in the oil and chemical industries.
- The total amount of railway track opened rose from 29,183 km in 1891 to 52,612 km in 1901.
- Income from industry shot up from 42 million roubles in 1893 to 161 million roubles by 1897.

Russia had started to catch up with other industrialised nations; by 1900, for example, Russia had ousted France to become fourth place in world iron production.

RAG – rate the timeline

Below are a sample exam question and a timeline. Read the question, study the timeline and, using three coloured pens, put a red, amber or green star next to the events to show:

- Red: events and policies that have no relevance to the question
- Amber: events and policies that have some significance to the question
- Green: events and policies that are directly relevant to the question

'Pobedonostsev did more than Witte to modernise Russia in the period from 1894 to 1917.' How far do you agree?

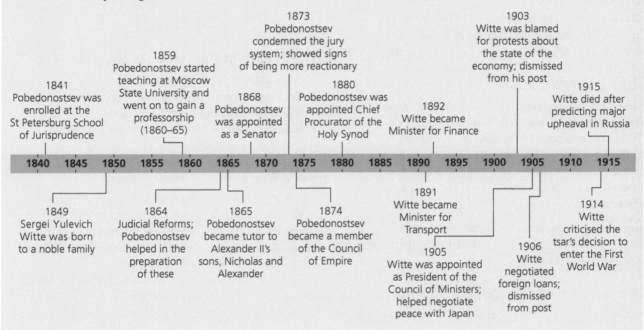

Eliminate irrelevance

Below are a sample exam question and a paragraph of an answer to the question. Read the paragraph and identify parts of the paragraph that are not directly relevant to the question. Draw a line through the information that is irrelevant and justify your deletions in the margin.

'Witte's greatest achievement was the negotiation of foreign loans.' How far do you agree?

Witte was born to a noble family in 1849. In 1891 he became Minister for Transport and then, in 1892, he became Minister for Finance. Witte's negotiation of foreign loans was a major achievement as it allowed for an injection of investment capital into industry. The result was that income earned from industry shot up from 42 million roubles in 1893 to 161 million roubles in 1897. Coal production doubled and that of iron and steel increased sevenfold. A major knock-on effect of this was the growth of the railway system: the total amount of railway track opened rose from 29,183 km in 1891 to 52,612 km in 1901. In 1903 Witte was blamed for protests about the mini-economic slump that occurred and was dismissed from his post. However, Witte went on to achieve success in the field of politics. For example, in 1905 Witte was appointed as President of the Council of Ministers and helped negotiate peace with Japan to end the Russo-Japanese War.

The Russo-Japanese War

Long-term causes

Prior to 1904 Russia and Japan had quarrelled for many years over Korea and Manchuria. Russia had looked to increase its influence in the Far East; of note was Russian success in negotiating a 25-year lease of the strategically placed Port Arthur from the Chinese in 1898.

Russia's threat to Japan increased with the construction of the Chinese Eastern Railway and occupation of Manchuria after a short military conflict with the Chinese. However, Russia agreed to withdraw military presence from Chinese territory by the beginning of 1903.

Short-term causes

Russia reneged on its promise to withdraw troops from Manchuria, which angered the Japanese. In February 1903 Japan retaliated by launching a night attack on the Pacific Squadron at Port Arthur. This escapade was something of a shambles, but it did result in damage to three Russian ships. It also seemed to have a negative effect on Russian morale.

Japan then proceeded to blockade Port Arthur. Preparations were made by both parties to participate in major land and sea battles.

The course of the Russo-Japanese War

● The Japanese moved north from Korea to confront Russia in southern Manchuria at the battle of Yalu. Outnumbered by about three to one, Russian forces were thoroughly beaten. This was an enormous shock to the Tsar and the other Great Powers.
● The siege of Port Arthur continued, isolating about 60,000 Russian troops. In December 1905, the port eventually surrendered.
● In May 1905 Rozhestvensky's Baltic Squadron, on its way to relieve Port Arthur, came up against Admiral Togo's fleet at the Tsushima Straits. This proved to be another terrible defeat for Russia and emphasised the technological superiority of the Japanese navy.
● The final straw for Russia came in 1905 with a humiliating defeat at Mukden. This prompted peace talks and the signing of a treaty.

Consequences of the war

The disastrous outcome of the Russo-Japanese War led to doubts being expressed about the ability of the tsar to maintain Russia's world status and concerns about the effectiveness of autocracy in general. The conflict with Japan was also followed by significant reform. This was because the Russo-Japanese War seemed to spark far more social unrest in the Russian homeland; Nicholas II made a number of economic, social and political reforms to appease protesters (see below).

The Treaty of Portsmouth, August 1905

This resulted in the following:
● Russia was forced to withdraw from Port Arthur, south Sakhalin and south Manchuria.
● Russian leaders had to acknowledge Japanese sovereignty in Korea.

Reforms

The war revealed that Russian military leaders had a lack of knowledge, understanding and skill in dealing with an enemy that, on paper, was vastly inferior. The Russian public associated such military incompetence with the tsar himself; this appeared to fuel discontent at home rather than to extinguish it, which had been one of the key aims of the war. Therefore, Nicholas II, rather reluctantly, introduced an element of democracy to Russia by setting up the *Duma* (see page 18). The hope was that the public would be convinced that the tsar was willing to become more accountable for his actions and those of his advisers. It is unlikely that this would have happened without the war, as the tsar was a staunch adherent of 'autocracy, orthodoxy and nationalism'.

Spectrum of importance

Below are a sample exam question and a list of general points which could be used to answer the question. Use your own knowledge and the information on the opposite page to reach a judgement about the importance of these general points to the question posed. Write numbers on the spectrum below to indicate their relative importance. Then write a brief justification of your placement, explaining why some of these factors are more important than others. This could form the basis of an essay plan.

'The Russo-Japanese War was a total disaster for Russia.' How far do you agree?

1 Military defeats (Port Arthur, Tsushima Straits, Mukden)

2 Loss of world status

3 Decline in the popularity of the tsar

4 Social unrest as a result of the war

5 The signing of the Treaty of Portsmouth

6 Political reforms (*Dumas*)

←——→

Least important   Most important

i **Turning assertion into argument** **a**

Below are a sample exam question and two sample conclusions. One of the conclusions achieves a high mark because it contains an argument (an assertion justified with a reason). The other achieves a lower mark because it contains only description (a detailed account) and assertion (a statement of fact or an opinion which is not supported by a reason). Identify which is which. The mark scheme on page 7 will help you.

To what extent was the Russo-Japanese War a result of Nicholas II's desire to show that Russia was a major world power?

Before 1904 Russia and Japan had argued for many years over Korea and Manchuria. Generally, Russia had looked to increase its influence in the Far East; Russia had success in negotiating a 25-year lease of the strategically placed Port Arthur from the Chinese. Russia's threat to Japan increased with the construction of the Chinese Eastern Railway. Nicholas II also sanctioned the occupation of Manchuria after a military conflict with the Chinese. However, Russia agreed to withdraw military presence from Chinese territory by the beginning of 1903, but went back on this promise, angering the Japanese. In February 1903 Japan retaliated by launching a night attack on the Pacific Squadron at Port Arthur. This attack was something of a shambles, but did damage three Russian ships. It also had a negative effect on Russian morale. Japan then proceeded to blockade Port Arthur. Preparations were subsequently made by both parties to participate in major land and sea battles.

It is a reasonable claim that Nicholas II viewed the Russo-Japanese War as an opportunity to remind the rest of the world that Russia was a great military, political and economic power. Much had been done to industrialise Russia and to reform the Russian army and navy. The war, in theory, gave Nicholas II the opportunity to show that Russia had modernised and could compete with the other major world powers (Britain, France and Germany in particular). This was reinforced by the Russian government's view that Japan would prove to be a far inferior enemy and an easy victory would ensue. However, probably more important was the practical and strategic issue of securing Port Arthur. Without the port Nicholas II would not have been able to fulfil his expansionist ambitions in the Far East. Also, given the social unrest that had been mounting in Russia, it is also possible that the tsar viewed the war as a chance to unite the people and take their minds off the challenges they faced.

The causes, nature and consequences of the 1905 Revolution

Causes of the revolution

Two areas of grievance arose against Nicholas II: the repressive nature of his government and his inability to deal with political, economic and social problems (including management of the Russo-Japanese War). As a result there was a steady rise in opposition, which culminated in the so-called revolutionary events of 1905. The opposition was characterised by:

- Growing support for political groups that were influenced by Populism and Marxism
- The actions of the liberal intelligentsia led by Struve
- Violence in the form of student unrest and the subsequent assassination of the Minister of Education (1901); strikes such as that at the Obukhov factory in St Petersburg (1901); peasant protests linked to poor harvests (1902); anti-war protests leading to the assassination of the Minister of the Interior, Plehve (1904)

The trigger for intensified action, resembling a revolution, was Bloody Sunday, 9 January 1905.

Course of events

The main events of 1905 were as follows:

- 3 January: Start of the Putilov strike, which sparked a wave of strikes across Russia
- 9 January: Bloody Sunday
- 4 February: Assassination of Grand Duke Sergei by Social Revolutionaries
- 5 February: Tsar promises political reform
- May: Establishment of the Union of Unions
- June: Establishment of the All-Russian Union of Peasants
- September: Mutinies in the army
- 8 October: Railway strike
- 13 October: Establishment of the St Petersburg Soviet
- 17 October: Issuing of the October Manifesto
- November: General strike in St Petersburg; Government storm the Soviet and arrest ringleaders
- December: Exiled radicals return to Russia (including Lenin)

Consequences

Not all historians agree that the events of 1905 constituted a revolution. This is worth bearing in mind when analysing the consequences of the events.

The October Manifesto

Mainly due to mounting opposition from liberals Nicholas II was advised by Witte to issue a new declaration of his policy, or manifesto. The October Manifesto was an attempt to clarify the powers that a new legislative assembly might have. It stated that:

- The assembly, or legislative *Duma* as it was called, would consist of elected representatives from the 51 provinces of the empire.
- The *Duma* would require the legalisation of political parties and trade unions.
- Russian people would be granted the right to freedom of assembly, worship and speech.

The Fundamental Laws

The October Manifesto seemed to satisfy the concerns of liberals, but only temporarily. In April 1906 Nicholas II announced the Fundamental Laws, which stated that: 'The Sovereign Emperor possesses the initiative in all legislative matters. No law can come into force without his approval.' In other words, Nicholas was determined to keep control of how the legislative *Duma* was to go about its work.

The *Dumas*

The creation of a *Duma* went in hand in hand with electoral reform. The vote was given to all men over the age of 25, but not to women or members of the armed forces. There was also a weakness of the new system as a whole: electoral districts within provinces were not equally represented.

Between 1905 and Nicholas II's abdication in March 1917, four *Dumas* were called. The first two consisted of representatives from a broad range of political groups and were highly critical of tsarist policies. As a result, Stolypin was ordered to change voting rights so that they favoured the nobility. Subsequently, the second two *Dumas* were very conservative and far more supportive of the government.

The first two *Dumas* lasted only months and, despite much heated debate over issues related to land distribution, they achieved little. The second two *Dumas* were more productive, however. They resulted in major reforms being made to the army and navy, improvements in the judicial system and the introduction of state-run insurance schemes for workers.

Introducing and concluding an argument a

Look at the key points of a possible answer to the question below. Then read the proposed introduction and conclusion.

- How effective is the introduction?
- How effective is the proposed conclusion?
- Could either be improved – especially in relation to Level 5 answers at AS-level or Level 6 at A-level?

To what extent did the events of 1905 constitute a revolution in Russia?

Key points:

- The nature and extent of protest throughout 1905 (marches, strikes, assassinations, mutinies) was unique
- The October Manifesto paved the way for a constitutional government
- The Fundamental Laws (April 1906) restricted the authority of the *Duma*
- The creation of the *Duma* led to electoral reform

Introduction:

Revolution can be defined as the sudden and permanent change in the way in which a country is governed and administered. With this in mind, the nature and extent of protest in 1905 that seemed to culminate in dramatic reforms might be seen to constitute a revolution. The October Manifesto and the resultant *Dumas* were clearly, in theory, measures that would lessen the autocratic power of the tsar and introduce an element of democracy to Russia. However, the introduction of the Fundamental Laws would suggest that Nicholas II had little intention of relinquishing his authority. In this respect the events of 1905 did not constitute a revolution.

Conclusion:

In conclusion, the marches, strikes, assassinations and mutinies did not equate to revolutionary activity and there was no revolution in the way politics, the economy and society were administered by the tsarist regime.

Develop the detail

Below are a sample exam question and a paragraph of an answer. The paragraph contains a limited amount of detail. Annotate the paragraph to add additional detail to the answer.

'The 1905 Revolution was mainly the result of economic problems.' How far do you agree?

The 1905 Revolution was due to economic problems to an extent. There was high unemployment and underemployment that led to rising poverty. Inflation also meant that people on low incomes suffered and struggled to buy the most basic consumer commodities. Of particular concern to peasants and workers were the relatively low levels of income they received for their efforts. The economic plight of peasants was also affected by a stupendous growth in the population, traditional farming techniques and ineffective policymaking. Workers became annoyed that on top of low wages they were forced to endure very long working hours and poor working conditions. However, the Revolution was not just about economic issues. Opposition had grown from a variety of groups mostly as a result of the repression instigated by Nicholas II's father. This was fuelled not just by concerns over the economy but also by Russia's decision to go to war with Japan.

Repression and reform under Stolypin

Repression under Stolypin: Stolypin's 'neckties'

Between the sitting of the first and second *Dumas*, a rather sinister development arose concerning the treatment of civilian protesters. After the arrest, trial and imprisonment of key Kadet and Labourist Party members for stirring up trouble in Finland by signing the Vyborg Manifesto, a new approach to dealing with such dissidents was adopted. The new Chairman of the Council of Ministers, Stolypin, thought that the approach to dealing with rebels was too slow, cumbersome and 'soft'. He therefore ordered a speeding up of the trial system for civilian rioters by introducing field court-martials. The result was a series of very quick trials and executions which gained the inglorious label of 'Stolypin's neckties'.

Table 1.1: The number of victims of terrorist activity (a) and the number of death sentences handed out to terrorists (b).

YEAR	KILLED (a)	WOUNDED (a)	SENTENCED (b)	EXECUTED (b)
1905	233	358	72	10
1906	768	820	450	144
1907	1231	1312	1056	456
1908	394	615	1741	825

Source: Peter Oxley *Russia 1855–1991*, page 72

Stolypin's land reforms

Rural unrest peaked during the years 1905–07. Nicholas II responded by instructing Stolypin, appointed as Prime Minister in 1906, to revamp government policy over land distribution. Stolypin's aim was to use land redistribution to build and strengthen the class of more able and educated, 'best' peasants. The hope was that they would then act as a role model for other peasants as well as a force against the *mir*. To this end the Stolypin reform (or 'wager on the strong' as it was sometimes called) involved the following:

● Unused or poorly utilised land was made available to the Peasant Land Bank (established in 1883). Forward-looking peasants could then buy the land from the bank on favourable terms.
● Peasants who were still farming strips (small plots spread over two to three fields) due to the strength of the *mir* were given the right to consolidate their land into smallholdings (small farm units). Hereditary household plots were not affected by this and it was also stipulated that land could not be immediately sold on to non-peasants. These provisos were designed to ensure that the mainstay of the Russian rural economy became the small, independent peasant farm.

In reality, the plan backfired due to the following reasons:

● The process led to an expansion in the numbers joining the wealthier class of peasants, who in theory would be more loyal to the tsar. However, they were not totally satisfied with the stipulations of the Stolypin reform, as they believed that the best land was still inaccessible to peasants.
● By 1914, about 2 million peasants had left the village communes, leaving some regions very short of rural labour. The First World War accelerated this trend. This exodus added to the challenge of maintaining supplies of food to the growing urban population.

Interpretations: content or argument?

Read the following interpretation and the two alternative answers to the question.

'Of Stolypin's devotion to peasants there can be no doubt. He was profoundly concerned with the human, moral and social future of the peasants on which he believed that the future of Russia depended.'

From: Hugh Seton-Watson, *The Russian Empire 1801–1917*, 1967

Which answer focuses more on the content and which focuses more on the arguments of the interpretation? Explain your choice.

This interpretation states that Stolypin was on the side of the peasants as he was devoted to them. He was very concerned about their welfare as he thought that if the peasants were well looked after they would work hard and help Russia become a strong country. I agree with this as Stolypin carried out quite a few reforms that helped peasants.

This interpretation argues that Stolypin recognised the importance of the peasants to the future well-being of Russia as a whole. It is inferred that if the welfare of the peasants was neglected then not enough food would be produced to feed the nation, especially those living in towns and cities. Therefore, Stolypin introduced land reforms and extended the Peasant Land Bank to encourage peasant farmers, especially the more able, to become entrepreneurial.

However, Stolypin's attitude towards the peasants was not based on altruism. He seemed to view peasants like any kind of worker; they were an economic resource that was needed for economic growth. This was especially true of the less wealthy peasants who, under the land reforms, were given extra but poorer-quality land than wealthier peasants. By 1914 about 2 million peasants had left the village communes to seek work in industrial areas, which suggests that Stolypin's reforms did little to improve their lot.

Simple essay style

Below is a sample exam question. Use your own knowledge and the information on the opposite page to produce a plan for this question. Choose four general points, and provide three pieces of specific information to support each general point.

Once you have planned your essay, write the introduction and conclusion for the essay. The introduction should list the points to be discussed in the essay. The conclusion should summarise the key points and justify which point was the most important.

To what extent were Stolypin's policies successful in dealing with the problems faced by Russia after 1905?

The political, economic and social situation in Russia in 1914

There was little reason to believe in 1914 that within three years, tsarism would have ended. In 1913 Russians had celebrated the tercentenary of the Romanov dynasty; the populace seemed to be supportive of the tsar to a degree not witnessed for some time. Nicholas II had indeed survived a number of challenges to his authority and seemed to be in a strong position to cope with the challenges of the First World War.

The political situation in Russia in 1914

Politically, Russia was relatively stable. The creation of the *Duma* via the October Manifesto had initially caused Nicholas II some difficulties, as participants in the new assembly took the opportunity to criticise tsarist policies. But the tsar, with the help of Stolypin, reduced the authority of the *Duma* and the challenge it posed faded.

The liberal members of the *Duma* were aggrieved by what happened, but did not feel it was correct to go openly against the tsar. The more radical groups in 1914 still lacked enough support to consider mounting a revolution and, besides, many of their leaders, such as Lenin, had been exiled.

The economic condition of Russia in 1914

From 1909 to 1914 the economy, as measured by its gross national product (GNP) had grown at an average annual rate of 3.5 per cent, although this was still sluggish when compared with that of Russia's European rivals. Also, there were still low levels of industrial productivity. Factories employed vast amounts of labour to compensate for a lack of investment in modern technology. Many workers continued to be employed in small-scale handicraft enterprise.

Agricultural production had increased and Stolypin's 'wager on the strong' had resulted in the number of peasant households becoming independent farms rising from over 42,000 in 1907 to 134,500 in 1913. However, by 1914 the figure had fallen to just under 98,000, suggesting peasants had started to leave the land to work and live in urbanised areas.

Russia's railway system had continued to develop so that by 1914, 70,160 kilometres of track existed (compared with 21,230 kilometres in 1881). However, the Trans-Siberian Railway had yet to be completed and parts of Russia were still unconnected to the 'centre'.

The state of Russian society in 1914

From 1897 (the time of the first census) to 1914, the population of Russia increased from 125 million to 166 million. This put pressure on those working on the land to increase the supply of food.

Urbanisation had occurred at a rapid pace, although about 80 per cent of the Russian population still lived in rural areas. Nicholas II had paid little attention to the working and living conditions of town dwellers. In 1914 there were just over 1,000 towns but only about 200 had piped water and 38 had a sewerage system. Even after improvements, disease continued to spread. An outbreak of cholera in St Petersburg in 1910 caused over 100,000 deaths.

Rising inflation, static wage levels and poor working conditions fuelled urban discontent. Economic and social changes had resulted in rising working–class consciousness and the potential for a challenge to tsarist authority from below. For example, the Lena Goldfields strike of 1912 was considered such a threat that the state sanctioned the killing of striking miners by troops.

Summarise the arguments

Below are a sample exam question and one of the interpretations referred to in the question.

Read the extract below and identify the interpretation offered. Look, in particular, for the arguments in the interpretation.

'On balance, tsarist Russia had recovered remarkably well from the traumatic events of 1905. Its prospects of stable evolutionary development in 1914 were good until foreign affairs intervened and Russia went to war.'

From: Jonathan Bromley, *Russia 1848–1917*

With reference to the interpretation and your contextual knowledge, how convincing do you find the extract in relation to the condition of Russia in 1914?

Interpretation offered by the source:

_____

_____

Recommended reading

Below is a list of suggested further reading on this topic.

- Orlando Figes, A People's Tragedy: *The Russian Revolution 1891–1924* (Bodley Head, 2014)
- Geoffrey Hosking, *Russia and the Russians* (Penguin, 2012)
- Michael Lynch, *Russia 1894-1941* (Hodder 2015)
- Richard Pipes, *Russia under the Old Regime* (Penguin 1995)
- Robert Service, *The Penguin History of Modern Russia: from Tsarism to the 21ˢᵗ Century* (Penguin, 2015)

Exam focus

REVISED

Below is a sample of a higher-level answer to an AS and A-Level-style essay question. Read the answer and the comments around it.

How stable was Russia in the period from 1906 to the outbreak of the First World War?

Stability implies that the state of a nation and/or empire is unlikely to change. Instability, therefore, might suggest considerable change that was either positive (moving a country forwards) or negative (moving a country backwards). After the so-called revolution of 1905–06, Russia did seem to enter into a period of economic, social and political stability and positive instability. The policies of Witte and Stolypin boosted the economy, the population in general continued to adulate the tsar (as shown by the tercentenary of the Romanov dynasty in 1913) and there was a decline in political agitation. However, this masked the fact that many issues were deep-rooted and appeared unresolved. In particular, the tsar's attempt to introduce democracy through the setting up of the *Dumas* was compromised by his insistence on maintaining autocracy. This left opposition to his rule to continue to grow albeit in a more concealed manner. By 1917 the critics of Nicholas II were in a position to call for his abdication. Hence, these developments could be judged to constitute negative instability.

Politically, Russia was relatively stable from 1906 to 1914. The creation of the *Duma* via the October Manifesto had initially caused Nicholas II some difficulties, as participants in the new assembly took the opportunity to criticise tsarist policies. But the tsar, with the help of Stolypin, reduced the authority of the *Duma* and the challenge it posed faded. The more liberal members of the *Duma* were concerned by the actions of Nicholas, especially his use of the 1906 Fundamental Laws and Stolypin's electoral reforms, but did not feel it was appropriate to openly oppose the tsar. The more radical groups in 1914 lacked support to consider mounting a revolution and simply resorted to criticising the *Dumas* from outside (many radicals were excluded from the first two *Dumas* as a result of reforms to the electoral system). Besides, their leaders, such as Lenin, had been exiled. Thus, relative to the situation during the war, especially in 1917, Russia displayed a fair amount of political stability. It was the events of 1914 to 1917 that created the most negative instability.

With respect to the Russian economy, there was evidence of positive instability in the sense that there was considerable economic growth; the economy was not in decline or stagnant but developing at a quite fast pace. From 1909 to 1914 gross national product (GNP) had grown at an average annual rate of 3.5 per cent, although this was still considered low when compared with that of Russia's European rivals (especially Germany and Britain). However, although the Russian textile industry, in particular, boomed there were still low levels of industrial productivity. Factory owners used huge labour forces rather than the latest technology to increase production; a major problem of this approach was that it was not efficient and by 1914 there was some indication of unstable, fluctuating levels of output. Also, swathes of workers continued to be employed in small-scale handicraft industries; this was evidence of stability (or even stagnation) rather than positive instability.

To serve mainly the needs of industry and agriculture, Russia's railway system had continued to be invested in; by 1914, 70,160 kilometres of track existed (compared with 21,230 kilometres in 1881). However, the Trans-Siberian Railway had yet to be completed and parts of Russia were still unconnected to the 'centre'. This amounted to some positive instability but with signs that, if Russia faced a crisis such as a world war, the transport system would be inadequate, resulting in negative instability.

This is a clear introduction that gives a good indication of how the candidate is going to tackle the question and come to an overall judgement. An interesting angle is taken on the word 'stability'.

The theme of political stability is well developed here; there is balanced analysis and some good support material that builds to an interim judgement at the end.

The economic theme is discussed in this section and it contains some sound explanation and evidence to support the comments made. Maybe the point about 'proto-industry' (small-scale handicraft industries) could have been developed further.

There is some sound comment evaluation here of the importance of railways to the Russian economy with, again, some interim judgement.

Quick quizzes at **www.hoddereducation.co.uk/myrevisionnotes**

Agriculture was another area of economic activity that displayed positive instability in that production had also increased. Much of this could be linked to Stolypin's 'wager on the strong', which resulted in a rise in the number of peasant households setting up independent farms from over 42,000 in 1907 to 134,500 in 1913. Independence in farming usually resulted in innovation and subsequent increases in production and productivity. However, by 1914 the number of independent farms had fallen to just under 98,000, suggesting peasants had started to leave the land to work and live in industrial towns and cities. This did not bode well for the capacity of the agricultural sector to cope with demands for more food due to the war, and indicates that the sector was drifting towards a state of negative instability.

> This paragraph covers the issue of agricultural activity and how it can be interpreted with respect to stability. Focus on the question is maintained and some analysis of the factor is incorporated at the end.

The population increase in Russia from 1897 (125 million) to 1914 (166 million) was stupendous and therefore not evidence of social stability. The rise put pressure on those working on the land to supply more food. Urbanisation had occurred at a rapid pace, although about four-fifths of the Russian population still lived in rural areas. Nicholas II had neglected the working and living conditions of ordinary town dwellers (that is, workers). By 1914 there were just over 1,000 towns but only about 200 had piped water and 38 had a sewerage system. Disease, associated with poor public health, spread. For example, an outbreak of cholera in St Petersburg in 1910 caused over 100,000 deaths. Rising inflation, low wage levels and poor working conditions added to urban discontent. Economic and social changes had resulted in rising working-class consciousness and the potential for a major challenge to tsarist authority from below. For example, the Lena Goldfields strike of 1912 was considered such a great threat that the state sanctioned the killing of striking miners by the police. This was hardly evidence of a stable society but one that was in a state of flux or negative instability.

> In this section, the argument about the degree of instability is further explained. Some links between the impact of economic growth and social change are made and a judgement is offered at the end.

In conclusion, there were many signs of a degree of political, economic and social stability and positive instability in Russia from 1906 to 1914. This can be supported by reference to the level of support the tsar appeared to have from the populace, and the way in which both industry and agriculture showed growth in production levels. However, Nicholas II's adherence to autocracy, the restrictions placed on radicals and some liberals and productivity issues in the economy seemed to lead to rising social negative instability. On the face of it, in the period from 1906 to 1914 Russia seemed relatively stable (and at times showed positive instability) but there were hidden signs that, if faced by a challenge such as the First World War, the tsarist system might collapse.

> The conclusion is an example of a solid judgement being made about the degree of stability in Russia from 1906 to 1914. It is congruent with the rest of the answer with no new material being added. The judgement is well developed and is indicative of a response that would reach a high level.

This is more than a well-explained list of factors. There is consistent focus on the key word in the question ('stable') and the command stem ('how'). The candidate uses a range of themes to structure their answer. Each theme is explained, supported and analysed and ends with an interim judgement about stability. Knowledge is used skilfully to develop an argument, rather than simply imparted. If there is one area of weakness, it is that some points are not fully developed. But, overall, this is a good example of a high level answer.

Interpreting key words

The answer gained a very respectable mark partly by taking a rather unique view of the word stability. The candidate's definition of 'stability' is made clear in the introduction but there are other ways of approaching the concept that would still lead to a mark at the highest level. Write an opening paragraph that interprets 'stability' in an alternative way but that also introduces a matching line of argument to be pursued.

Exam focus

REVISED

Below is a sample of a higher-level answer to an AS-style interpretation question. Read the answer and the comments around it

'Despite efforts at political reform, urban Russia on the brink of the First World War arguably found itself on the brink of a new revolution.'

From: O. Figes, *Revolutionary Russia 1891–1991*, 2014

Evaluate the strengths and limitations of this interpretation, making reference to other interpretations that you have studied.

This interpretation is arguing that in the towns and cities, revolution was likely in Russia in 1914. It argues that although the government had made some attempts to calm the population through political reform, these had not worked, and that the people seemed ready to rise up. However, this interpretation emphasises that urban Russia was on the brink, and that the government had made attempts at reform. Other interpretations stress the continuity and stability in this period – that, on the brink of the First World War, Russians were ready to unite and fight for the tsar – while another interpretation is that different localities in Russia were more susceptible to revolutionary feeling than others in 1914.

> The candidate shows a good understanding of the message of the interpretation. The response then proceeds to indicate an awareness of the wider debate over the background to the revolutions of 1917.

This interpretation can be seen to be valid to some extent because, by 1914, there had been growing tensions in urban Russia for several years, and demands for reform were growing every day. The number of days lost to strikes in the towns and cities grew significantly in the period to 1914, and there was growing violence accompanying these strikes. The terror tactics used by the regime after the death of Stolypin in 1911 only furthered the cause of the revolutionaries. Indeed, even the moderate and liberal leaders acknowledged that peaceful attempts at reform had failed and revolution might be the only answer.

> Here the candidate uses contextual knowledge to evaluate the validity of the interpretation. The information used is fully relevant; it is not simply imparted but is woven into the analysis presented.

This view is given further credence by the failure of attempts at political reform, since the *Duma* became a mere talking shop, with members pleading with the tsar to give them more control over their own affairs. Tensions reached a head in the summer of 1914 when a general strike was called, which members of the *Duma* openly supported. The interpretation correctly acknowledges there were efforts at political reform, but that these were heavily controlled by the tsar's own advisers, to the extent that election results were doctored.

> Further evaluation of the strengths of the interpretation is offered with, again, sound application of contextual knowledge.

However, this interpretation misses the point about the fundamental stability of the tsarist regime in 1914, and its resilience in the face of adversity. Most importantly, the troops remained loyal to the tsar and the revolutionary groups were either still in exile or on the fringe of the political scene. This meant that the cities were relatively safe, and despite the violence of 1914, the revolutionary threat did not really exist.

> The candidate moves on in this section to provide some balanced comment on the interpretation. A weakness is highlighted, with focus on a key point that the historian appears to have overlooked.

Furthermore, the interpretation ignores the improved economic outlook in the urban centres in 1914, and the lack of real efforts at political reform. Economic growth in the years to 1914 was 6 per cent annually, and Russia became a major textile manufacturer. Political reform beyond the creation of the *Dumas* did not exist, and the October Manifesto had not weakened the authority of the tsar at all. Finally, the interpretation ignores the fact that the withering away of opposition to the tsar when war was declared, the open support for his regime and the army, the silence of opposition in the *Duma* and the ending of strikes, all showed that Russia was far from on the brink of revolution at that time.

More balanced analysis and evaluation is in evidence here, with direct reference being made to the interpretation. Contextual knowledge is once again used very effectively to show how the interpretation compares to others (the improved state of the economy, political stability and the low level of activity from opposition groups).

There is a very good understanding of the debate and how the given interpretation fits into the wider debate about the motives for the cultural developments. The interpretation is clearly evaluated, and detailed own knowledge is applied to the interpretation, particularly in support of it. The response does evaluate both the strengths and limitations of the interpretation and would reach a high level at AS.

Evaluating an interpretation

Answers to Interpretation questions should start by placing the given interpretation in the wider context of the historical debate about the issue. This interpretation expresses the idea that urban Russia was still on the verge of revolution despite the changes that had occurred in the political system. If the interpretation read 'Efforts at political reform in Russia by the start of the First World War meant that the conflict was unlikely to fuel a further revolution', how would you then frame your response? Write a detailed plan for the new interpretation that indicates how you would evaluate it.

2 The 1917 Revolutions

The impact of the First World War (1914–17)

REVISED

A useful way of analysing the impact of the First World War on Russia is to consider two schools of thought: the so-called 'optimist' and 'pessimist' schools. The optimists argue that tsarism was resilient to the forces of change. It needed a dramatic and unique event to change the nature of Russian government completely. The pessimists argue against the First World War being a significant turning point, seeing it rather as the event that speeded up the demise of the Romanovs.

Defeats

The best chance of Russian military success was probably at the start of the war. However, the terrible defeats at Tannenberg and the Masurian Lakes resulted in the lowering of morale of the Russian troops. Russian soldiers had fought well but they were let down by the poor strategic decision-making of General Samsonov and General Rennenkampf. By the end of 1915, Stavka, the command centre for the Russian army, blamed lack of military progress on the 'shells crisis', but it was more the case that military administrators did not have the ability to cope with the logistical challenges posed by the war.

Further defeats and the subsequent Great Retreat in 1915 prompted Nicholas II to take personal control of the armed forces.

Although Russia's war effort seemed to improve throughout 1916, the failure of the Brusilov offensive and the emergence of attrition warfare indicated that the tsar was not capable of bringing the conflict to a satisfactory end.

Losses

The Russians lost twice as many troops as the enemy during the early campaigns and the hope at home that Russia would score an early victory waned. Russian casualties for the whole of the war were around 8 million, including 1.7 million dead and 2.4 million captured.

Economic dislocation

The whole of the Russian economy was geared up to win the war. This had a negative impact on the lives of Russian people, as industry and agriculture could not cope with the demands of the war.

Food shortages

Throughout the war period, the average output of cereals was higher than it had been during the first decade of the twentieth century. But a rising population, food requisitioning by the army, a fall in the availability of fertilisers and transport problems all worked together to create food shortages, especially after 1916. For example, in St Petersburg – now renamed Petrograd to appear less German and more Russian – the bread ration fell 25 per cent in the first three months of 1916.

Transport problems

The food issue was made worse by communication and transport problems. It was not surprising that stockpiling of supplies occurred; piles of foodstuffs rotted away and, at Archangel (in northern Russia), the 'mountains' of hardware were so great that they started to sink into the ground!

Inflation

The total cost of the war was in the region of 3 billion roubles, which far exceeded levels of government expenditure during peacetime. In 1913, for example, government expenditure was about 1.5 billion roubles. The cost was met partly through borrowing (foreign loans, war bonds), increases in tax (income, excess profits) and printing more money. Some of these measures were partly responsible for rampant inflation. By 1917 prices had risen 400 per cent from the start of the war; those on fixed incomes (the low-paid and elderly) suffered greatly.

Spot the mistake

Below are a sample exam question and a paragraph written in answer to this question. Why might an examiner not give this paragraph much credit? What is wrong with the focus of the answer in this paragraph?

'The First World War simply speeded up the demise of the Romanov dynasty.' How far do you agree?

The First World War did indeed seem to speed up the demise of the Romanovs; there were clear indications that before the war Nicholas II was struggling to maintain his authority. This is supported by historians labelled as 'optimists'. The optimists argue that tsarism and autocracy, by definition, were extremely resilient to the forces of change. It needed a dramatic and unique event to completely change the nature of Russian government. The First World War fitted the bill perfectly. The optimists claim that Russia was never able to get to grips with the demands of the world's first industrial war (that is, the first large-scale war to be fought using the products of industrialisation) and it was inevitable that the Russian people would point the finger of blame towards those who led them into the conflict. Furthermore, without the war, the tsar would have coped with the demands for further constitutional reform and, gradually, changes to government would have occurred to quieten the critics. This was already a trend that had started, particularly from 1905 onwards, and there was little reason to believe that further progress would not be made.

Complete the paragraph

Below are a sample exam question and one paragraph of an answer. The paragraph contains a point and specific examples, but lacks a concluding analytical link back to the question. Complete the paragraph, adding this link back to the question in the space provided.

'The most serious consequence of the First World War for the Russian people was a shortage of food.' How far do you agree?

Obtaining adequate food supplies was a major problem for the Russian people, especially after 1916. Throughout the war period, the average output of cereals was substantially higher than it had been during the first decade of the twentieth century. However, a rapidly rising population, food requisitioning by the army, a fall in the availability of fertilisers and transport problems all worked together to create food shortages. Some historians have pointed out that this was largely a regional problem; those in Petrograd suffered more than others with, for example, their bread ration falling 25 per cent in the first three months of 1916. But regional variation is not particularly important, as the social unrest that resulted from high prices and shortages gathered momentum in the places where it was likely to have the greatest impact — the growing towns and cities in the west of Russia. Overall,

_____

_____

Influences on the leadership of Nicholas II

Alexandra (1872–1918)

In 1894 Princess Alexandra married Nicholas II and subsequently took on the title of Empress of Russia. Alexandra was the German granddaughter of Queen Victoria, which caused suspicion among the Russian peoples. The Empress had inherited the haemophilic gene from her grandmother and passed it on to her son Alexei. This was significant, as it was to influence her relationship with the religious mystic, Rasputin.

Alexandra was deeply religious and was quick to adopt the Russian Orthodox Church. Her faith influenced her attitude towards the royal court, which she thought was too ostentatious, and towards peasants, with whom she sympathised.

From 1915 Nicholas II took control of the Russian military and was away at the Eastern Front for much of the time. This left the governance of Russia in the hands of Alexandra and Rasputin, who by this time had become a personal adviser to the Empress. The historian Orlando Figes has claimed Alexandra then became 'the real autocrat in the capital', although she was encouraged by her 'holy friend' who 'used her as a mouthpiece for his own pretensions to power.' This caused much discontent within the government; a 'Progressive Bloc' had emerged which put pressure on the tsar to take firmer control of proceedings.

Rasputin (1871–1916)

Gregory Efimovich Rasputin was born in Western Siberia to a peasant family. He spent some time in an Orthodox monastery before travelling around Russia. In 1903 he arrived in St Petersburg and quickly gained a reputation as a mystical healer, but also as a sexual predator. In 1905 he had been introduced to the tsar and tsarina as someone who might be able to cure Alexei of his illness. After becoming acquainted with Rasputin, Alexei's health did seem to improve, which endeared the monk to Alexandra. His increasing influence over the royal family led to him being despised by the tsar's advisers. In 1916 he was murdered, under strange circumstances, by a group of aristocrats.

The Fourth *Duma*, November 1912–February 1917

The final *Duma* was dominated once more by politicians from the far right. Its rule coincided with heightened and brutal repression of civil disorder. This was characterised by state police killing striking miners at the Lena Goldfields (1912). The murders outraged many *Duma* members who viewed this as a retrograde step by the government in its attempt to deal with Russia's economic and social problems. Guchkov, leader of the moderate Octobrists, warned the tsar and ministers that the Russian people had become revolutionised by the actions of the government and that they had lost faith in its leaders. In 1914 the *Duma* made the following proclamation and prophecy of doom:

'The Ministry of the Interior systematically scorns public opinion and ignores the repeated wishes of the new legislature. The *Duma* considered it pointless to express any new wishes in regard to internal policy. The Ministry's activities arouse dissatisfaction among the broad masses that have hitherto been peaceful. Such a situation threatens Russia with untold dangers.'

The final *Duma* became infamous for eventually putting pressure on the Tsar to abdicate and went on to form the backbone of the short-lived Provisional Government. However, despite its criticisms of government rule, it remained an institution that was dominated by the 'old guard'.

Delete as applicable

Below are a sample exam question and a paragraph of an answer to the question. Read the paragraph and decide which of the possible options (in bold) is most appropriate. Delete the least appropriate options and complete the paragraph by justifying your selection.

How important was Tsarina Alexandra in influencing Russian government from 1915 to 1917?

> Tsarina Alexandra was **not very/somewhat/very** important in influencing Russian government after 1915. This was due to the fact that the tsar had decided to take personal control of the army and located himself at the Eastern Front, thus leaving the day-to-day administration of affairs in the hands of his wife. The situation was **helped/hindered/complicated** by the tsarina's involvement with the Russian mystic, Rasputin. The historian Orlando Figes is **partly/mostly/entirely** correct in claiming that Alexandra's holy friend used her as a mouthpiece for his own pretensions to power. However, Figes also states that the tsarina became the 'real autocrat in the capital', suggesting that she was **unable/only partly able/able** to keep Rasputin in check, although some have questioned that. There was also **little/some/a great deal of** concern in government circles about the consequences of the tsar's and tsarina's decision-making. In particular, the so-called 'Progressive Bloc' called for Nicholas to return to the capital to reassert his authority.

Spider diagram

Read the question and construct a spider diagram to identify relevant reasons. Complete the spider diagram with a sentence of explanation for each reason, then prioritise your reasons by adding numbers to each oval box – with 1 as the most important reason and 6 as the least important.

'The fourth *Duma* was unsuccessful mainly due its inability to stop the unfair treatment of protesters from 1912 to 1917.' How far do you agree?

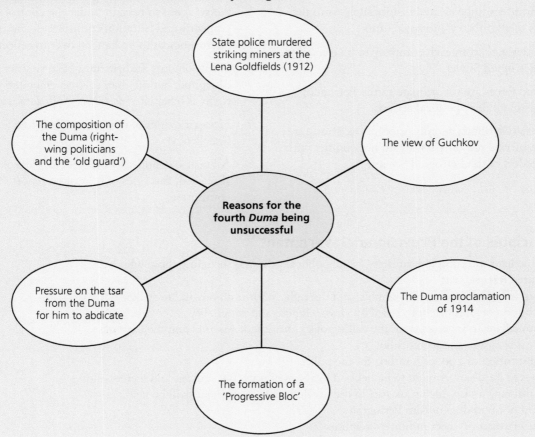

The events of February and March 1917

Main events

The events of February and March 1917 culminated in the abdication of the tsar and the imposition of a Provisional Government.

- 9 January 1917 – About 150,000 workers took to the streets of St Petersburg to celebrate the anniversary of Bloody Sunday.
- 18 February 1917 – A strike occurred at the Putilov Steel Works.
- 19 February 1917 – Bread rationing was introduced.
- 23 February 1917 – Marchers celebrating International Women's Day and workers from the Putilov plant combined to protest about poor working and living conditions.
- 25 February 1917 – A general strike took place, with workers being fired on by troops. Rodzianko, president of the *Duma*, urged the tsar to change his attitude towards governing.
- 27 February 1917 – The Petrograd Soviet (workers' council) was formed alongside the Provisional *Duma* Committee. This was the foundation of governance through a dual authority and a clear indication that the tsar was considered unfit to rule by a majority of senior politicians.
- 1 March 1917 – Soviet Order No. 1 was passed, which gave the Petrograd Soviet total control over the Russian military. Soviet Order No. 1 frightened the authorities as it gave the impression that workers were about to use military support to seize power.
- 2 March 1917 – Under pressure from close advisers and family members, and after his brother refused to take the throne, Nicholas II decided to abdicate. An official Provisional Government was formed to deal with the crisis until elections to a Constituent Assembly could be held. On 3 March it announced the principles by which it would rule in the newspaper *Izvestiia*.

Soviet Order No. 1:

1 Committees to be elected immediately from the ranks of all military and naval units

2 One delegate from each company to be elected to the Petrograd Soviet

3 Armed forces are subordinate to the Petrograd Soviet in all their political actions

4 Orders of Military Commission of the Duma are to be carried out only if they do not conflict with the orders of the Petrograd Soviet

5 All weapons to remain under the control of company and battalion committees, and in no circumstances to be handed over to officers

6 While on duty soldiers must observe strict military discipline, but off-duty soldiers enjoy the same rights as other citizens; saluting off-duty is abolished

7 Honorific titles of officers are abolished (e.g. Your Excellency)

8 All coarse conduct by officers towards soldiers is abolished, and cases of it must be reported to the committee.

The principles of the Provisional Government

1 An immediate and complete amnesty for all political prisoners including those who had committed terrorist acts

2 Freedom of speech, press, and assembly, and the right to form unions and to strike

3 The abolition of all restrictions based on class, religion, and nationality

4 The immediate arrangements for the calling of a Constituent Assembly on the basis of universal suffrage and secret ballot

5 The substitution of a people's militia for the police

6 Elections to local government to be held on the basis of universal suffrage and secret ballot

7 Those military units which took part in the revolutionary movement shall be neither disarmed nor withdrawn from Petrograd

8 The preservation of strict military discipline

Support or challenge?

Below is a sample exam question which asks how far you agree with a specific statement. Below this is a series of general statements which are relevant to the question. Using your own knowledge and the information on the opposite page, decide whether these statements support or challenge the statement in the question.

‘The events of February and March 1917 made the appointment of a Provisional Government inevitable.’ How far do you agree?

	Support	Challenge
18 February 1917 – A strike occurred at the Putilov Steel Works.		
19 February 1917 – Bread rationing was introduced.		
23 February 1917 – Marchers celebrating International Women's Day and workers from the Putilov plant combined to protest about poor working and living conditions.		
25 February 1917 – A general strike took place, with workers being fired on by troops.		
27 February 1917 – The Petrograd Soviet was formed alongside the Provisional *Duma* Committee.		
1 March 1917 – Soviet Order No. 1 was passed, which gave the Petrograd Soviet total control over the Russian military.		

Simple essay style

Below is a sample exam question. Use your own knowledge and the information on the opposite page to produce a plan for this question. Choose four general points, and provide three pieces of specific information to support each general point.

Once you have planned your essay, write the introduction and conclusion for the essay. The introduction should list the points to be discussed in the essay. The conclusion should summarise the key points and justify which point was the most important.

To what extent was the ‘dual authority’ of the Petrograd Soviet and the Provisional Government doomed to fail from the start?

The Provisional Government and the Petrograd Soviet

The Provisional Government

The turn of events in February and March had not been expected (see page 32). In theory, the abdication of Nicholas and the formation of the Provisional Government marked the end of autocracy in Russia. In practice, the move towards greater democracy was short-lived, and the governance of Russia was soon dominated by a single individual, Lenin.

Some historians have argued that the era of the Provisional Government was the only time that the Russian Empire was united. Others have pointed out that, although this may be true, it was unlikely from the start that the new government would be able to sustain unity.

Challenges faced by the Provisional Government

- The Provisional Government was self-appointed and not democratically elected. It consisted mainly of the 'old guard': most were members who had previously served in the *Duma* of 1912 and who were conservative in outlook. This was not a problem for the members of the government, as their mission was to establish a Constituent Assembly.
- Authority was shared with the Petrograd Soviet who, from the start, opposed most of what the Provisional Government proposed.
- The set of eight principles by which the government would rule were liberal in nature. Russia was said to have become 'the freest of the belligerent countries'. However, the downside for the Provisional Government was that it allowed the proliferation of protest groups, the most dangerous being the Bolsheviks.
- Economic issues such as runaway inflation, low real wages and the length of the working day proved very difficult to deal with.

- The peasant land issue dragged on throughout the Provisional Government's time in office. The best solution it could provide was to argue that, due to the nature of the land redistribution problem, only a properly elected assembly could deal with it.
- There was continuous disagreement between the Provisional Government and the Petrograd Soviet over Russia's involvement in the war. The former wanted to push on for 'a decisive victory' whilst the latter demanded 'peace without annexations or indemnities' but also 'revolutionary defensism'. This rift was never resolved and was a major reason for the eventual failure of the government.

An attempt to bridge the differences between the two competing authorities was made in May 1917 with the formation of a coalition government. This was led by Prince Lvov, who invited six members of the Petrograd Soviet to join. But it did little to appease the more radical members of the Soviet and the problems faced by the ruling body continued. National elections to a Constituent Assembly were postponed, the land issue was ignored, workers' committees were clamped down on and involvement in the war continued. All of this combined to produce a further decline in support for the Provisional Government and rising militancy within the Petrograd Soviet.

The demands of the Petrograd Soviet

By June 1917 members of the Soviet were demanding even more involvement in the national government. Some supporters of the Soviet had adopted the slogan 'All Power to the Soviets' and this sentiment was strongly expressed during the sittings of the first All-Russian Congress of Soviets. This shift in stance appeared to be a significant threat to the continued existence of the government.

Eliminate irrelevance

Below are a sample exam question and a paragraph of an answer to the question. Read the paragraph and identify parts of it that are not directly relevant to the question. Draw a line through the information that is irrelevant and justify your deletions in the margin.

'The Petrograd Soviet had a huge influence on work of the Provisional Government.' How far do you agree?

The influence of the Petrograd Soviet on the Provisional Government was significant, although to describe it as 'huge' would be an exaggeration. This is partially illustrated by the continuous disagreement between the Petrograd Soviet and the Provisional Government over Russia's involvement in the war. The former wanted to push on for 'a decisive victory' whilst the latter demanded 'peace without annexations or indemnities' (but also 'revolutionary defensism'). Protests against the war heightened and reached a disturbing peak in July when the sailors at Kronstadt mutinied. The rift was never resolved and was a major reason for the eventual failure of the government. An attempt to bridge the differences between the two competing authorities was made in May 1917 with the formation of a coalition government. This was led by Prince Lvov, who invited six members of the Petrograd Soviet to join. Prince Lvov was from one of the most respected noble families. However, it did little to appease the more radical members of the Soviet and the problems faced by the ruling body continued. National elections to a Constituent Assembly were postponed, the land issue was ignored, workers' committees were clamped down on and involvement in the war continued. All of this combined to produce a further decline in support for the Provisional Government and rising militancy within the Petrograd Soviet.

Introducing and concluding an argument

Look at the key points of the answer. How good are the proposed introduction and conclusion? Could either be improved?

Assess the reasons why the Provisional Government struggled to impose its authority in the early months of its rule

Key points:
- The Provisional Government was unelected
- The eight principles of the Provisional Government were very liberal
- From the beginning the Provisional Government had to share power with the Petrograd Soviet
- The government inherited a number of problems, including inflation and peasant land demands
- The debate over Russia's involvement in the First World War impeded attempts to face other challenges

Introduction:

Probably the main reason for why the Provisional Government struggled to impose its authority from the beginning was that it had little option but to share power with the Petrograd Soviet. This was particularly the case after the workers' council had issued Soviet Order No. 1, which gave them control over the armed forces. From this stemmed other problems that the Provisional Government had to face, particularly the war: it was very difficult for the government to get an agreement with the Soviet over whether Russia should continue with its war efforts. At the same time there were a number of inherited economic and social challenges that fed into the situation created by the emergence of a dual authority.

Conclusion:

In conclusion, the Provisional Government struggled in the early years of its rule for a multitude of reasons. Its failure to deal with the challenges it faced at the start meant that it was to struggle to survive for more than a year.

The return of political exiles and the April Theses

The return of Stalin and Kamenev

Changes made by the Provisional Government facilitated the revival of political groups such as the Bolsheviks, whose leaders had been in exile. Stalin and Kamenev moved back to Petrograd from exile in Siberia in March 1917, and Lenin moved back from Switzerland in April 1917. By this time, disagreements within the Bolshevik party had arisen over the significance of the events of February and March.

The views of Stalin and Kamenev	The views of Lenin
Kamenev, in particular, believed in accommodationism (co-operating with the Provisional Government and the other groups that pressed for reform). Stalin and Kamenev thought Russia's participation in the First World War should be ended by encouraging the Provisional Government to enter peace negotiations with Germany.	Lenin believed there should be no co-operation with the Provisional Government and other parties. Lenin believed that Russia's participation in the First World War should be ended by encouraging soldiers from all countries to mutiny and help other workers overthrow their governments.

When Lenin arrived on 3 April, as leader of the Bolsheviks, he immediately went about clarifying what the party stood for.

The return of Lenin

Lenin's return was significant for the following reasons:
- He had been aided by the German government to get back to Russia; German leaders hoped that a successful Bolshevik revolution would lead to Russia withdrawing from the war. Those who opposed the Bolsheviks viewed Lenin's acceptance of help from Germany as an act of collusion with the enemy.
- He made it clear to party members that he was against the Provisional Government and that it should be overthrown.

The day after his return Lenin set out his ideas, in his April Theses, on how the Bolshevik party should proceed.

The April Theses

The main thrust of the April Theses was that it:
- condemned the Provisional Government for being bourgeois and demanded that it should be overthrown
- proposed abandoning co-operation with other political parties
- called for a seizure of power by the soviets, creating a genuine workers' government. However, Lenin also viewed the soviets as a rival power base; by acknowledging their importance, he believed that it would provide an opening for the Bolsheviks to infiltrate and control them.

Lenin urged that 'Old Bolsheviks' who opposed the Theses should leave the party. He then went on to reinforce his message through the use of two propaganda slogans:
- 'All Power to the Soviets' (the soviets should take control of governing Russia)
- 'Peace, Bread and Land' (peace – withdraw Russia from the war with Germany; bread – tackle food shortages; land – deal with peasant concerns over land distribution).

Lenin linked the slogans to his opposition to the Provisional Government. The latter had persisted with the war effort to the detriment of the workers and peasants, who were hungry and who clamoured for a fairer property-owning system. According to Lenin, only the soviets could resolve these issues.

Spectrum of importance

Below are a sample exam question and a list of general points which could be used to answer the question. Use your own knowledge and the information on the opposite page to reach a judgement about the importance of these general points to the question posed. Write numbers on the spectrum below to indicate their relative importance. Having done this, write a brief justification of your placement, explaining why some of these factors are more important than others. The resulting diagram could form the basis of an essay plan.

How important was the return of political exiles in March–April 1917 as an influence on the actions of the Provisional Government?

1 The return of Stalin and Kamenev in March and then Lenin in April resulted in them coming together to discuss policy differences.

2 Lenin took the lead to clarify the Bolshevik stance on the Provisional Government and the war.

3 Lenin published his ideas in the April Theses.

4 The April Theses condemned the Provisional Government for being bourgeois and demanded that it should be overthrown.

5 Lenin used slogans to undermine the Provisional Government.

6 The Provisional Government was influenced by other developments, most notably the growing strength of the Petrograd Soviet.

←————————————————————————————————————→
Least important   Most important

 Turning assertion into argument   **a**

Below are a series of definitions, a sample exam question and two sample conclusions. One of the conclusions achieves a high mark because it contains an argument. The other achieves a lower mark because it contains only description and assertion. Identify which is which. The mark scheme on page 7 will help you.

- **Description:** a detailed account.
- **Assertion:** a statement of fact or an opinion which is not supported by a reason.
- **Reason:** a statement which explains or justifies something.
- **Argument:** an assertion justified with a reason.

To what extent did the return of Lenin to Petrograd in March 1917 hinder attempts by the Provisional Government to deal with the challenges it faced?

When Lenin arrived on 3 April as leader of the Bolsheviks, he immediately went about expressing clearly what the party stood for. The day after his return he set out his ideas, in his April Theses, on how the Bolshevik party should proceed. He criticised the Provisional Government for being bourgeois and demanded that it should be overthrown. He also proposed abandoning co-operation with other political parties and called for a seizure of power by the soviets, creating a genuine workers' government. All of this meant that he hindered the Provisional Government in its attempts to deal with the problems it faced.

In conclusion, the return of Lenin to Russia in April 1917 did hinder the work of the Provisional Government in the sense that the Bolshevik leader was able, mainly through his April Theses, to stoke up opposition. In particular, Lenin's criticism of the Provisional Government's attitude towards the war and that he considered the government to be bourgeois seemed to gain the backing of a considerable number of Bolsheviks. However, it is important not to exaggerate the importance of Lenin's return. Not all of the leading Bolsheviks agreed with him and the party as a whole was yet to gain the support it was to have in October. In this respect, Lenin's return only had a marginal influence on the work of the Provisional Government. More of a hindrance was the challenge of the Petrograd Soviet coupled with the drain on resources as a result of Russia's involvement in the war.

Kerensky, the July Days and the Kornilov Revolt

Kerensky

In an attempt to rejuvenate support for the Provisional Government after its disagreements with the Petrograd Soviet in the early summer of 1917, Prince Lvov, the prime minister, sanctioned a new war offensive. Under the guidance of Kerensky, the Minister for War, the offensive was launched on the south-western front. It failed miserably, with the Russian forces experiencing heavy losses and many soldiers deserting. Lvov was blamed and he was subsequently replaced by Kerensky.

The July Days

Protests against the war heightened and reached a disturbing peak in July when sailors at Kronstadt mutinied. At this point, there were many opponents of the government, most notably the Bolsheviks, who believed that the Soviet needed to seize power. The Mensheviks and SRs refused to support this idea, and in the end troops loyal to Lvov saved the day by clearing the streets of Petrograd of the protestors. Kerensky emerged from this with credit; despite the failures of the army in the war, troops had been organised successfully to quell internal rebellion. As a result, on 8 July he was appointed prime minister. Kerensky launched a 'reaction' against those involved in the 'July Days' rising. The Bolsheviks became the target for repression; their newspaper, Pravda, was banned, leading members were either imprisoned or exiled and the party as a whole was branded as being treacherous.

The Bolsheviks

Kerensky seemed to have beaten off the Bolshevik threat, but two developments quickly undermined his achievements.

The land question

One was a shift in Bolshevik policy towards the peasant land question. Until the 'July Days', the Bolsheviks believed that a revolution could only be generated through the industrial proletariat. However, as an increasing number of peasants started to take land illegally, Lenin and other Bolshevik leaders realised that they could exploit this activity by claiming it was truly revolutionary. By promoting a Land to the Peasants campaign, the Bolsheviks quickly gained support from rural workers and seemed to promise a solution to the land question, which the Provisional Government had failed to do.

The Kornilov Revolt

The second major challenge to Kerensky occurred in August when the military commander, Kornilov, marched with his troops to Petrograd with the intention of forcefully closing down the Soviet. Kerensky seemed to believe that Kornilov, having defeated the Soviet, would then move on to take over the Provisional Government and impose a military-style dictatorship. Kerensky, therefore, agreed to the Bolsheviks being given arms to defend Petrograd. In the end, a bloody conflict was averted. Railway workers refused to transport Kornilov's army making it difficult for the commander to mobilise his troops. Kornilov also received advance warning of how quickly the Bolsheviks had mobilised their defences and decided that the proposed takeover had a good chance of ending in disaster. He therefore abandoned his plan and was arrested.

The Kornilov affair was significant for two reasons.
- Firstly, the Bolsheviks were viewed as heroes for organising the protection of Petrograd.
- Secondly, it was evident that the Provisional Government was susceptible to being challenged by the military and, therefore, others who might want to use force to seize power.

After the affair, the Bolsheviks quickly gained more support so that by early September they had majorities in both the Petrograd and Moscow Soviets. By the end of October they had ousted the Provisional Government and taken control of Petrograd.

Simple essay style

Below is a sample exam question. Use your own knowledge and the information on the opposite page to produce a plan for this question. Choose four general points, and provide three pieces of specific information to support each general point.

Once you have planned your essay, write the introduction and conclusion for the essay. The introduction should list the points to be discussed in the essay. The conclusion should summarise the key points and justify which point was the most important.

'Kerensky was the main reason for the fall of the Provisional Government in October 1917.' How far do you agree?

Develop the detail a

Below are a sample exam question and part of an answer to this question. The paragraph contains a limited amount of detail. Annotate the paragraph to add additional detail to the answer.

How successful was Kerensky in dealing with the challenges he faced from July to September 1917?

As Minister of War, Kerensky was only partially successful. When he moved on to become Prime Minister, he did well to deal with the unrest that was occurring, although he struggled to get to grips with the peasant land question. He also found it difficult to deal with direct challenges to the Provisional Government such as that posed by General Kornilov. Kornilov threatened a military coup against the Provisional Government. Kerensky responded by arming members of the Petrograd Soviet to help resist the challenge. By the autumn of 1917 Kerensky's actions could be seen to have led to further challenges to his authority.

The events of October 1917

The course of the October Revolution of 1917

By 8 September the Bolsheviks were in control of the Petrograd Soviet. By the middle of September, they also controlled the Moscow Soviet. The Bolsheviks had made monumental progress towards governing Russia. The main events leading to the final Bolshevik takeover in 1917 were as follows:

- 7 October: Lenin returned from exile, having fled after the failure of the July days.
- 10 October: The Bolsheviks began planning for a revolution.
- 23 October: Kerensky closed *Pravda* and *Izvestiia*; a round-up of leading Bolsheviks was attempted.
- 24 October: The Petrograd Soviet's **Military Revolutionary Committee** began to seize power under the command of **Trotsky**.
- 26 October: The members of the Provisional Government were arrested, except for Kerensky, who fled (later to settle in the USA).
- 27 October: The **All-Russian Congress of Soviets** (in session since 25 October) was informed by Lenin that the Bolsheviks had seized power.
- 2 November: The Bolsheviks had total control of Moscow.

Reasons for the success of the Bolsheviks

The Bolsheviks were successful in gaining power for the following reasons:

- The defeat of General Kornilov (see page 38) meant the Bolsheviks were seen as heroes.
- The refusal of the Bolsheviks to work with the Provisional Government ensured that they distanced themselves from unpopular policies such as the continuation of the war (see page 38).

Bolshevik opposition to the creation of a Constituent Assembly

The majority of members of other parties wanted a short-term government based on consensus, with the main aim of creating a Constituent Assembly. The leading Bolsheviks rejected this, arguing that such an arrangement would continue to favour 'old interests' to the detriment of workers and peasants.

Changes made by the Provisional Government

The initial changes made by the Provisional Government allowed for the revitalisation and expansion of political groups. This especially favoured the Bolsheviks, whose leaders had been in exile for some time but who returned with a vengeance. Stalin moved back to Petrograd from exile in Siberia in March 1917 and Lenin from Switzerland in April 1917. Lenin moved quickly to publish his April Theses in which he condemned the Provisional Government for being bourgeois and called for a seizure of power by the Soviet.

Bolshevik use of propaganda

Bolshevik leaders cleverly used propaganda to appeal for support from both workers and peasants. The slogan 'All Power to the Soviets' promised workers (including soldiers and sailors) control of the political system. This was coupled with the slogan 'Bread, Peace and Land', which targeted peasants. Lenin changed his mind about peasant support. Originally, he saw peasants as a hindrance to any potential revolution as he thought they were apathetic and stupid. But their appropriation of land illegally displayed a certain revolutionary zeal, which Marx and Lenin had not predicted. Lenin therefore decided peasant support was worth having and could be exploited by the Bolsheviks. The actions of the peasants contributed partly to Lenin's adaptation of Marxism to create Marxism–Leninism.

The role of Kerensky

The Provisional Government, both under Prince Lvov and Kerensky, struggled to deal with the Bolsheviks. Although leading Bolsheviks were exiled or imprisoned after the disturbances of the July Days, Kerensky inadvertently strengthened their position by indirectly involving them in the resolution of the Kornilov affair. On 7 October, Lenin returned once more to Petrograd to plan for a revolution. Kerensky waited until 23 October to order another round-up and deportation of Bolsheviks but it was too late. The next day, the establishment of the Petrograd Soviet's Military Revolutionary Committee (MRC) was announced. By the end of October, Lenin and the MRC (headed by Trotsky) had disbanded the Provisional Government, exiled Kerensky and announced to the Congress of Soviets that the Bolsheviks had seized power.

RAG – rate the timeline

Below are a sample exam question and a timeline. Read the question, study the timeline and, using three coloured pens, put a red, amber or green star next to the events to show:
- Red: events and policies that have no relevance to the question
- Amber: events and policies that have some significance to the question
- Green: events and policies that are directly relevant to the question.

'The events of September and October 1917 suggest that the Bolshevik takeover of government was a popular uprising.' How far do you agree?

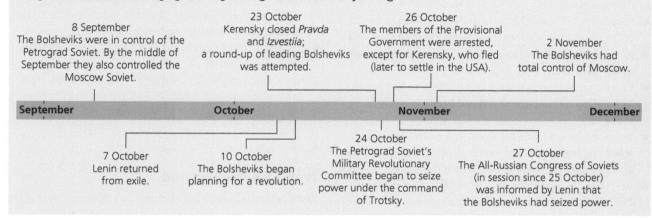

8 September
The Bolsheviks were in control of the Petrograd Soviet. By the middle of September they also controlled the Moscow Soviet.

23 October
Kerensky closed *Pravda* and *Izvestiia*; a round-up of leading Bolsheviks was attempted.

26 October
The members of the Provisional Government were arrested, except for Kerensky, who fled (later to settle in the USA).

2 November
The Bolsheviks had total control of Moscow.

September | October | November | December

7 October
Lenin returned from exile.

10 October
The Bolsheviks began planning for a revolution.

24 October
The Petrograd Soviet's Military Revolutionary Committee began to seize power under the command of Trotsky.

27 October
The All-Russian Congress of Soviets (in session since 25 October) was informed by Lenin that the Bolsheviks had seized power.

Support your judgement   a

Below are a sample exam question and two basic judgements. Read the exam question and the two judgements. Support the judgement that you agree with more strongly by adding a reason that justifies the judgement.

'The main reason for the Bolsheviks' takeover of power in October 1917 was their effective use of propaganda.' How far do you agree?

> *Overall, the Bolsheviks' use of propaganda, especially slogans, was crucial to their obtaining control of the government in October 1917.*
>
> _____
>
> _____

> *Generally, Bolshevik leaders used propaganda skilfully to promote their ideas but there were other, more important factors which influenced how they were able to seize power in October 1917.*
>
> _____
>
> _____

Tip: Whichever option you choose, you will have to weigh up both sides of the argument. You could use phrases such as 'whereas' or words like 'although' in order to help the process of evaluation. Also, notice the use of the word 'seize' in the second statement. How valid is that word when analysing what the Bolsheviks did in October 1917?

The roles of Lenin and Trotsky

The role of Lenin in the build-up to the 1917 revolution

Lenin's role can be traced back to at least 1900, when he joined the Social Democratic party. After that his influence can be seen through:

- his position as editor, from 1900 to 1903, of the main newspaper of the revolutionary movement, *Iskra* (*The Spark*)
- his publication of *What is to be Done?* (1902), a collection of ideas about how Russia should be ruled
- his leadership of the Bolsheviks as a breakaway group in the SDs (from 1903 onwards)
- his return to Russia from exile in 1905 to witness the 'revolution' (although he did not become actively involved)
- his exile abroad from 1906 to 1917; from a position where he was not threatened by imprisonment he was able to continue to gain support for the Bolshevik cause
- his return to Russia in 1917 after the overthrow of Nicholas II in February, which gave momentum to the Bolsheviks
- the publication of the April Theses, which set out his plan to take power.

Although Lenin was in exile for long periods, he was a great influence on the revolutionary movement as a theorist. He was instrumental in the Bolshevik seizure of power and the establishment of communist rule in Russia. Through his writings and oratory skill Lenin gave a sense of urgency to the efforts of the Bolsheviks to overthrow the Provisional Government. His claim that 'History will not forgive us if we do not assume power' was based on concerns that the Bolsheviks would lose their chance to rule if they allowed:

- the validation of the election results to the Constituent Assembly
- the October meeting of the All-Russian Congress of Soviets to dictate the future of the governance of Russia.

By persuading his Bolshevik colleagues, in September, to act quickly to physically take power from the government, he ensured that the Constituent Assembly and the Congress would be in a weak position.

The role of Trotsky in the build-up to the 1917 revolution

Trotsky's role can be traced back to 1905, when he was first appointed as chairman of the St Petersburg Soviet. After that, his influence can be seen through:

- his period in exile (1907–17), when he developed his ideas about **Permanent Revolution**
- his resumption in September 1917 as chairman of the Petrograd Soviet
- his position as one of three co-ordinators of the Military Revolutionary Committee (MRC)
- his management of the **Red Guards**.

Trotsky's background

Trotsky started his political career as a Menshevik. In 1905 he was appointed chairman of the St Petersburg Soviet but was arrested and exiled until 1917. During his exile he produced his theory of Permanent Revolution. Trotsky believed that the introduction of communism to Russia would not be successful unless it spread also throughout the world.

When Trotsky returned to Russia he joined the Bolshevik party and was also appointed chairman of the Petrograd Soviet. He then proceeded to become the organiser of the October Revolution. On 9 October, in his position as chairman, he influenced the Petrograd Soviet to set up the Military Revolutionary Committee (MRC). This essentially meant that the Soviet had the means to control Petrograd. Trotsky built on this by organising the Red Guards. Once Lenin gave instructions for the revolution to begin, the Red Guards were used to take control of the strategic locations of government in Petrograd.

Develop the detail

Below are a sample exam question and a paragraph written in answer to this question. The paragraph contains a limited amount of detail. Annotate the paragraph to add additional detail to the answer.

> Who had more influence on the events of 1917: Lenin or Trotsky? Explain your answer.

Both Lenin and Trotsky had significant roles to play in the events of 1917, but in different ways. Both were intellectuals and theorists and introduced ideas that influenced the revolutionary movement in 1917. However, Lenin's views were probably considered more significant as he was the leader of the Bolsheviks. A major difference between the two concerned the methods that they adopted to prepare the Bolshevik party for the takeover of the Provisional Government. Lenin directed operations and tried to persuade fellow Bolsheviks, using his oratory skill, of the need to use force to achieve their aims. Trotsky, on the other hand, used his administrative skills, under Lenin's guidance, to prepare the party for the actual takeover of power.

Recommended reading

Below is a list of suggested further reading on this topic.

- Isaac Deutscher, *The Prophet Armed: Trotsky 1879–1921* (Oxford University Press, 1959)
- John Laver, *Lenin, Liberator or Oppressor* (Hodder 1994)
- Michael Lynch, *Trotsky, The Permanent revolutionary* (Hodder, 1995)
- Derrick Murphy, *Lenin* (Collins, 2005)
- Christopher Read, *Lenin* (Routledge, 2005)
- Robert Service, *Lenin: A Biography* (Macmillan, 2000)
- Ian Thatcher, *Trotsky* (Routledge, 2003)

Exam focus

Below is a sample of a higher-level answer to an AS and A-Level-style essay question. Read the answer and the comments around it

Assess the reasons why the overthrow of the tsar in March 1917 was followed by a second Revolution in October 1917.

After the overthrow of Tsar Nicholas II in March 1917, the running of Russia was placed in the hands of the Provisional Government. The aim of this government was to pave the way for the creation of an elected Constituent Assembly, and it was successful in doing that. However, the Provisional Government struggled to deal with the challenges it faced and the Bolsheviks eventually exploited this to organise the second revolution of October 1917. Although the revolution was primarily the result of Bolshevik strengths relative to the weaknesses of the Provisional Government, the context within which the struggle occurred (the First World War) also needs to be considered.

The major weakness of the Provisional Government was that it lacked legitimacy. It was an unelected body made up mainly of a mixture of liberal and conservative-minded politicians who served in the final *Dumas* of 1912–17. The only radical member was the Socialist Revolutionary, Kerensky. This meant that whenever the government struggled to tackle a problem its opponents were quick to question its authority and competence. It was seen by the Bolsheviks, in particular, as a government not fit to rule.

Connected to the lack of legitimacy was the fact that the Provisional Government's power was lessened by having to share governance with the Petrograd Soviet. From the start, the Soviet, through its issuing of Soviet Order No. 1, undermined the authority of the Provisional Government. For example, when the government argued for an all-out effort to gain a decisive victory in the First World War, this was opposed by the Soviet. The latter called for a peace to be negotiated 'without annexations or indemnities' and an insistence on defending the principles established after the March revolt against the tsar. The ability of the Soviet to act as a foil against the demands of the Provisional Government was especially significant as it was commandeered and utilised by the Bolsheviks. Realising the level of support the Soviet had from workers, Lenin and other leading Bolsheviks infiltrated and dominated the Soviet's leadership. This gave the Bolsheviks a strong platform from which to overthrow the Provisional Government.

In a way, the Provisional Government allowed the Bolsheviks and other opponents to gain momentum through the eight principles upon which it aimed to govern. These principles were 'liberal' in nature; the immediate and complete amnesty granted to all political prisoners including those who had committed terrorist acts and the granting of freedom of speech, press and assembly, in particular, allowed the Bolsheviks to regroup and accelerate their challenge to a government they viewed as bourgeois.

A major criticism of the Provisional Government that was levelled by the Bolsheviks was that it failed to show urgency in dealing with economic and social problems. Falling real wages, rampant inflation and difficult working conditions had become grievances of urban workers and the Bolsheviks exploited this by promising change. Coupled with this was the fact that the peasant land issue was allowed to drag on; the Provisional Government's solution was to argue that only a properly elected assembly could deal with it. Peasants took the initiative and started to grab land from the major landowners illegally. This again was something that Lenin, through his April Theses, was able to exploit. He promised that land distribution would occur under a Bolshevik government in the hope this would win over support from the countryside.

A clear introduction that sets the scene and outlines three key factors that help explain why there was a second Revolution in October 1917.

A weakness of the Provisional Government is clearly stated and explained.

This is a well-developed paragraph that focuses on another weakness of the Provisional Government. It also links this to the opportunism of the Bolsheviks to form an argument.

Here, the theme of weakness of the Provisional Government is linked to the 'eight principles'. There is sound explanation of how and why the opponents of the government were able to exploit the principles.

More linkage here; Provisional Government weakness is measured once more against Bolshevik opportunism.

In May 1917 a coalition government was formed between the Provisional Government and the Petrograd Soviet, but the problems faced by the ruling body continued. Prince Lvov attempted to deal with the war issue by ordering Kerensky, as Minister of War, to carry out a new offensive. This failed and resulted in Kerensky replacing Prince Lvov as Prime Minister. Kerensky used force to put down riots during the 'July Days', but was less successful in dealing with an attempted coup, led by General Kornilov. Although Kornilov failed to achieve his aim, he was only deterred by the actions of railway workers who refused to transport the General's troops and by the arming of members of the Petrograd Soviet by Kerensky. This resulted in workers gaining confidence and authority; the Bolsheviks then realised that if they could control the Soviet they were likely to be successful in deposing the Provisional Government. Thus, the increasing inability of the Provisional Government to deal with the challenges it faced, and the misjudgement of Kerensky in particular, resulted in the Bolsheviks increasing their support and strengthening their position.

However, it must be stressed that the Provisional Government inherited many of the problems it faced, especially those connected to the First World War. The war was a huge economic drain on Russia. It cost Russia about 3 billion roubles, which was far in excess of government expenditure during peacetime. In 1913, for example, government expenditure was about 1.5 billion roubles. The cost was met partly through borrowing, increases in tax and printing more money. The inflation that resulted (by 1917 prices had risen 400 per cent from the start of the war) hit those on fixed incomes the greatest. Low-paid workers suffered greatly and were quick to blame the Provisional Government. Both the Bolsheviks and, as importantly, the Petrograd Soviet fed off this discontent to formulate, in October, what is sometimes referred to as a popular rising.

Finally, without a strong and able leadership the Bolsheviks would never have been able to successfully challenge the Provisional Government. Lenin was clever in using propaganda to gain support from both workers and peasants. The slogans 'All Power to the Soviets' and 'Bread, Peace and Land' gave hope to workers and peasants of a better future. Of equal significance was the establishment of the Petrograd Soviet's Military Revolutionary Committee (MRC). By the end of October, Lenin and the MRC (headed by Trotsky) had disbanded the Provisional Government, exiled Kerensky and announced to the Congress of Soviets that the Bolsheviks had seized power. This would not have been possible if Lenin and Trotsky had not had the skill to manipulate the circumstances to their advantage. However, this can still be linked to the ineptitude of the Provisional Government. The Bolshevik leaders had only been exiled (and not imprisoned). They found moving back into Russia to exploit periods of crisis relatively easy. In this respect the Provisional Government had only itself to blame for its eventual demise.

The second revolution in October 1917 was undoubtedly due to the inability of the Provisional Government to deal with the challenges it faced. However, many of these issues were not of its own making. In particular, the problem of Russia's poor showing in the First World War was a result of Nicholas II's decision-making. On the other hand, the Provisional Government was associated with the old tsarist regime; both the Petrograd Soviet and the Bolsheviks were able to exploit to gain the level of support required to assume power.

This section gives attention to the role of Kerensky and infers that he was responsible for some of the difficulties faced by the Provisional Government. There is more well-developed explanation and argument which suggests that this response to this point is encouraging. There is also an attempt at judgement towards the end.

This paragraph develops the argument about the importance of context and how the Provisional Government could be seen as a victim of circumstance. There is some very solid analysis here, especially at the end of the section.

Here we have some impressive analysis, evaluation and judgement about the role of the Bolsheviks in the October Revolution. The view of how Lenin was able to exploit the weaknesses of the Provisional Government is sustained.

A solid judgement is made about the reasons for the October Revolution. It is very much in line the rest of the answer, with no new material or viewpoint being added. The judgement is well explained and is indicative of a high level response. The answer shows linkages throughout and there is consistent focus on 'reasons why' which are assessed with respect to their relative importance. Knowledge is not just imparted but is used to support an argument. This is a good example of a high level answer.

Exam focus

Below is a sample of a higher-level answer to an A-Level-style mini-essay question. Read the answer and the comments around it.

Which of the following had more influence on Nicholas II's downfall in March 1917?

(i) Criticism from the *Duma*

(ii) Rasputin

Explain your answer with reference to (i) and (ii).

Both the Fourth *Duma* and Rasputin influenced Nicholas II's downfall in March 1917. It was the reconvened *Duma* of 1915 that actually persuaded Nicholas to abdicate, but it was Rasputin's behaviour that undermined the tsar's position during the First World War.

> A nicely phrased opening paragraph; the two factors to be discussed are evaluated and linked.

As a result of electoral reforms made by Stolypin, both the third and fourth *Dumas* were dominated by conservative politicians and those who in general supported Nicholas. However, by the time of the fourth *Duma*, social unrest had heightened and the tsar had resorted to wide-scale repression to restore law and order. Of particular note was the Lena Goldfields incident of 1912. Miners at Lena went on strike and were attacked by the state police and troops; an estimated 200 miners were shot dead. This, coupled with a growing number of strikes elsewhere, caused consternation among the moderate members of the *Duma*. Guchkov, leader of the Octobrists, warned the tsar and ministers that the Russian people had become revolutionised by the actions of the government and that they had lost faith in its leaders. Despite this, the *Duma* showed support for the tsar by volunteering to be suspended due to the outbreak of war. This suggests that in 1914 criticism from the *Duma* was unlikely to have had much influence on Nicholas II's decision-making.

> This is a well-explained, carefully developed and supported paragraph. It ends with a judgement that is in line with the preceding commentary.

The poor Russian showing in the initial stages of the war encouraged the *Duma* to ask to be recalled. Nicholas agreed but became flustered when *Duma* politicians asked him to replace his cabinet of ministers with people who could restore national confidence. Nicholas refused, which led to the formation of the Progressive Bloc, a body within the *Duma* that became fixated on persuading the tsar to make concessions. Some cabinet reshuffling did take place and Nicholas attempted to restore support for his policies by, in 1915, taking personal command of the Russian military. The decision failed to improve Russia's standing in the war and by February 1917 protests and strikes intensified. Nicholas was advised by the president of the *Duma*, Rodzyanko, to make major changes to the government but the tsar refused and dissolved the *Duma*. The resultant Provisional Committee, formed from the Progressive Bloc, demanded that the tsar should abdicate. When generals close to the tsar also suggested he stand down, it was the final nail in the coffin for Nicholas. On March 2 the decree of abdication was signed. Thus, criticism and pressure from the *Duma*, especially after 1915, was instrumental in the downfall of the tsar.

> A bit of description and narrative mixed with some analysis here. However, this approach does serve the purpose of showing how the actions of the *Duma* led to the abdication of Nicholas II and is very much in line with the introduction.

However, Nicholas's stubbornness in dealing with the *Duma* and his weak decision-making was also to blame for his demise. By taking personal control of the war effort in 1915 he neglected his duties as supreme leader of the Russian empire. This paved the way for the tsarina and her adviser, Rasputin, to gain influence over the governance of Russia. Alexandra's German background and Rasputin's reputation as a charlatan created great mistrust among the Russian people. Coupled with the uneasiness over how the war was progressing, the concerns over governance did much to weaken the tsar's position.

> This is a well-explained paragraph. It blends discussion of Nicholas's attitude towards the *Duma* with his decision-making ability. It highlights the link between the tsar's move to take control of the military in 1915 with the influence of Rasputin.

Rasputin's role in Russian affairs was clearly significant in influencing views about whether Nicholas was fit to rule. In 1903 he had arrived in St Petersburg with a reputation as a mystical healer, but also as a person who could charm others, especially women, to accept his ideas. In 1905 he had been introduced to the tsar and tsarina as someone able to cure Alexei (the tsar and tsarina's son) of his illness. After being 'treated' by Rasputin, Alexei's health seemed to improve, which endeared the monk to Alexandra. His increasing influence over the tsarina led to him being despised by the tsar's advisers. Some ministers, such as Sturmer, believed that Rasputin became so powerful that he was able to sway the appointment of government officials who were his 'friends'. Such people were usually incompetent and easily manipulated by the monk.

Although he was mistrusted, Rasputin did show a pragmatic approach to administration. His common-sense reorganisation of the military's medical supply system gained him some plaudits. But, as some historians have argued, by displaying a certain degree of organisational competence Rasputin highlighted the weaknesses of tsarist bureaucracy. It was probably this, rather than any supposed relationship with Alexandra, that led to Rasputin's murder by a group of nobles in December 1916. Rasputin was an indicator of the kind of personality needed to rescue Russia from the mire and, in this sense, he influenced the downfall of Nicholas II.

The pressure from the fourth *Duma* on Nicholas II to resign, alongside that exerted by military leaders, was very important, as it was this that led directly to the final abdication in March 1917. Nevertheless, Nicholas, with hindsight, made some poor tactical decisions which allowed the tsarina and Rasputin to have a good deal of influence over the government. The *Duma* was directly responsible for Nicholas's downfall, while Rasputin was more symbolic of the reasons why the *Duma* challenged the tsar's authority.

A very solid explanation of Rasputin's importance is given in this section.

The idea expressed here, about the Rasputin controversy being an indicator of all that was wrong about the way Russia was being ruled, is quite a sophisticated one, suggesting further that the response is likely to receive a high mark.

The response finishes with an evaluation and judgement that builds on the main body of the answer. It is not, as many conclusions are, a mere summary of what has been said in the essay.

The response deals with both of the stated factors, shows how they are linked and arrives at a judgement about the importance of each. There is some drift to description (although the material is entirely relevant) which detracts a little from the overall quality of the answer. Overall, this is a good solid response and would gain a high level.

Reaching a judgement

In order to reach the higher levels, you must reach a judgement as to which factor was the more important. This response argues that both factors were important but in different ways. Use the information in the answer to rewrite the conclusion to argue that Rasputin had more influence than the *Duma* on Nicholas II's downfall in March 1917.

3 The Civil War and Lenin

The Constituent Assembly

REVISED

Although the Bolsheviks had claimed **de facto** rule, they knew they had to allow the elections to the planned Constituent Assembly to proceed. The Bolsheviks hoped they would win a clear majority to legitimise their position. When this did not materialise, it created the same problem for Lenin that had existed for the tsar and the Provisional Government – how to deal with opposition. The results of the election clearly showed that the degree of 'opposition' was substantial.

Table 3.1: Results of the election of the Constituent Assembly.

Party	Votes	Seats
SRs	17,490,000	370
Bolsheviks	9,844,000	175
National minority groups	8,257,000	99
Left SRs (pro-Bolshevik)	2,861,000	40
Kadets	1,986,000	17
Mensheviks	1,248,000	16
Total	**41,686,000**	

Source: M. Lynch, *Reaction and Revolution: Russia 1881–1924*, Hodder Education (2004).

Lenin believed that the Bolsheviks would not be able to achieve and consolidate power through future elections to the Assembly and therefore chose to use military force to end it. The official justification for such action was that the elections had been rigged, but also that conceding power to such an Assembly '… would again be compromising with the malignant bourgeoisie. The Russian soviets place the interests of the toiling masses far above the interests of treacherous compromise disguised in a new garb.'

Lenin claimed that the Constituent Assembly was 'elected on the old register' and 'appeared as an expression of the old regime when the authority belonged to the bourgeoisie'. In other words, the electoral system that was adopted, the list of candidates that could be voted for and the subsequent result was similar to what happened with the tsarist Duma. Lenin used this to justify shutting down the Assembly after one day; there was no popular demonstration against this move.

The role of the Third All-Russian Congress of Soviets

In January 1918, the Third All-Russian Congress of Soviets sanctioned the closure of the Constituent Assembly, and also proclaimed the establishment of the **Russian Soviet Federative Socialist Republic** (RSFSR). The RSFSR was essentially the Great Russia of the old Empire but was now to be ruled without a monarch (hence the use of the term 'republic').

However, this did not put an end to opposition to the Bolsheviks. If anything, it increased it and also caused concerns to be expressed within the party over the methods adopted by Lenin. The reaction against Lenin was further strengthened by his desire to take Russia out of the First World War and strike a peace deal with Germany. The left-wing SRs in particular viewed Lenin as a traitor to the revolution and a German collaborator.

Interpretation: content or argument?

Read the following interpretation and the two alternative answers to the question.

'Had the Constituent Assembly remained in session for more than one day in January 1918 it would have challenged the legitimacy of the Bolshevik government. It had an SR majority and would have reflected agrarian socialist values and a government elected by the Assembly would have been a coalition government.'

From: Martin McCauley, *Russia 1917–1941*

Which answer focuses more on the content and which focuses more on the arguments of the interpretation? Explain your choice.

This interpretation states that the Constituent Assembly would have been successful if it had been allowed to exist for more than one day in January 1918. It would then have gone on to challenge whether the claim to power by the Bolsheviks was valid. This seems to be a reasonable view. In the Assembly the SRs had 370 seats, compared to 175 won by the Bolsheviks, which meant that the SRs would have been able to persuade an elected government that its policies, especially on agriculture, were the best ones to follow.

This interpretation argues that it if the Constituent Assembly had been allowed to exist beyond the one day in January 1918 then the Bolsheviks would not have been able to control the government of Russia. This is likely to be true as the Bolsheviks gained a minority of seats in the Assembly and would have had no option but to have agreed to the formation of a coalition government. Lenin and the Bolsheviks would then have had a major check on their aspirations to create a government dominated by one party which would promote Leninist ideology.

However, the extract argues with hindsight. Although it is true that the SRs gained far more votes than the Bolsheviks in the elections to the Assembly, the Bolsheviks also quickly responded by shutting down the Assembly. Thus, the argument goes against the facts, which means it is not totally convincing.

Spot the mistake **a**

Below are a sample exam question and a one-paragraph answer. Why might an examiner not give this paragraph much credit? What is wrong with the focus of the answer in this paragraph?

Assess the reasons for the closure of the Constituent Assembly by the Bolsheviks in January 1918.

In January 1918, the Third All-Russian Congress of Soviets agreed to the closure of the Constituent Assembly, and also announced the establishment of the Russian Soviet Federative Socialist Republic (RSFSR). The RSFSR was essentially the Great Russia of the old Empire, but was now to be ruled without a monarch (hence the use of the term 'republic'). However, opposition to the Bolsheviks did not end. If anything, it increased, and concerns were expressed within the party over the methods adopted by Lenin to silence the Assembly. The reaction against Lenin was further strengthened by his desire to take Russia out of the First World War and strike a peace deal with Germany. The left-wing SRs in particular argued that Lenin was a traitor to the revolution and a German collaborator.

Issues faced by the Bolsheviks at the end of 1918

The Bolsheviks introduced a new constitution in July 1918. Before then, there were a number of issues that they had to deal with to allow them to consolidate their position. These included: initial opposition from a mixture of liberals, Mensheviks, SRs and royalists; land ownership; and the war.

Opposition: The Second All-Russian Congress of Soviets

The Second All-Russian Congress of Soviets met on 25 October. Right-wing SRs and Mensheviks, who favoured a coalition government, walked out of the Congress in protest. This left the Bolsheviks with little opposition and a clear mandate to rule.

Opposition: The 'Petrograd revolution'

The October Revolution was a Petrograd revolution. The Bolsheviks, therefore, had to spread their authority. They attempted to do this by creating more soviets in towns and cities across Russia. This proved difficult due to opposition from the 'old guard'; resistance throughout the empire was a major reason for the outbreak of a civil war that was to last until 1921.

Land ownership: The Decree on Land

Shortly after taking control from the Provisional Government, the Bolsheviks issued the Decree on Land (November 1917). It sanctioned the requisition of private land by peasants, but stated that the division and redistribution could only be carried out by village soviets. It was very similar to what rival SRs had proposed for years, and therefore went some way to winning over the support of the Bolsheviks' opponents.

War: The Decree on Peace

The Bolsheviks issued a Decree on Peace (October 1917), which called for an immediate truce and a peaceful settlement. This laid the foundation for an **armistice** that was signed on 2 December 1917. Although Germany insisted on harsh terms for a final settlement, Lenin still argued strongly in favour of a treaty. On 3 March 1918 the Soviet representative, Sokolnikov, signed the Treaty of Brest-Litovsk, which ceded a huge portion of territory, amounting to about a third of European Russia, to Germany, including Ukraine, Russia's most important grain-producing region. Russia also agreed to pay **reparations** of 3 billion roubles. Trotsky called the treaty a **diktat**.

The end of the war

In August 1918 Germany's campaign on the Western Front collapsed and it soon withdrew its troops from Russia completely. The Brest-Litovsk agreement became meaningless and Lenin then had the chance to rid the party of those who opposed him.

Complete the paragraph

Below are a sample exam question and a paragraph written in answer to this question.

The paragraph contains a point and specific examples, but lacks a concluding analytical link back to the question. Complete the paragraph, adding this link back to the question in the space provided.

How far had Lenin consolidated power by the end of 1918?

Lenin knew that once the Bolsheviks had closed the Constituent Assembly he had to move quickly to justify and consolidate his authority. He did this by creating a new Constitution in 1918, promoting the spread of soviets, issuing a number of Decrees (on Land and on Peace) and negotiating Russia's withdrawal from the First World War. The Decree on Land was particularly important as it won over support from SRs, many of whom had campaigned for the fairer distribution of land to peasants and for this to be organised by the soviets. Overall,

_____

_____

 Delete as applicable

Below are a sample exam question and a paragraph written in answer to this question. Read the paragraph and decide which of the possible options (in bold) is most appropriate. Delete the least appropriate options and complete the paragraph by justifying your selection.

How important was the Decree on Peace in enabling Lenin to agree favourable terms with Germany for Russia's withdrawal from the First World War?

The Bolsheviks issued a Decree on Peace, which called for **an immediate/a phased** truce and a peaceful settlement. This **partly/mostly/wholly** laid the foundation for an armistice that was signed on 2 December 1917. Although Germany insisted on **fair/reasonable/harsh** terms for a final settlement, Lenin still argued **moderately/strongly** for a treaty to be signed. On 3 March 1918 the Soviet representative, Sokolnikov, signed the Treaty of Brest-Litovsk, which ceded a **small/huge** portion of territory, amounting to about **a quarter/a third/two-thirds** of European Russia, to Germany, including Ukraine, Russia's most important grain-producing region. Russia also agreed to pay a **small/moderate/huge** amount in reparations of 3 billion roubles. Trotsky called the treaty a diktat.

The origins and course of the Russian Civil War (1918–21)

The origins of the Russian Civil War

The origins of the war can be traced to Russia's involvement in the First World War and the Russian Revolution.

The Bolsheviks' seizure of power in October 1917 sparked chaos throughout what was still the Russian Empire. Different political and regional groups reacted according to their individual wants and needs – some saw the October Revolution as an opportunity to launch a counter-offensive against the Bolsheviks, while others moved to attempt to gain long-awaited independence from Russian central government. The single event that probably signalled the start of the war was Kerensky's Petrograd offensive to try and retake the capital in October. This was suppressed with relative ease, but other shows of resistance proved more challenging. The fact that the Civil War lasted more than four years is testament to the scale and magnitude of the forces that were determined to overthrow Lenin and his comrades.

The main events of the Russian Civil War

The following events show how the Civil War unfolded.

The early stages of the Civil War (November 1917–November 1918)

- November 1917: Kerensky's and General Krasnov's offensive was brought to a halt.
- Spring 1918: Opposition from Cossacks in the region of the Don and the Urals was nullified.
- April 1918: Having defeated General Kornilov's volunteer army, Lenin proclaimed that the war was about to end. Foreign intervention occurred in this month when British marines were sent to support those opposing the Bolsheviks.
- May 1918: The Czech Legion, on its way to Vladivostok, revolted and became a focus for those who wanted to strengthen their efforts against the Red Army. The SRs, in particular, were keen to ally with the Czechs.
- August 1918: Trotsky signalled his intent in ensuring the cohesiveness of the Red Army by executing deserters. The Bolsheviks became concerned at the arrival of more foreign troops, this time from the USA.

- September 1918: The Directory government (of those opposed to the Bolsheviks) emerged at Ufa. It was made up primarily of SRs and Czechs. By this time, opposition fighting forces were known as the White armies.
- November 1918: Admiral Kolchak announced himself Supreme Ruler of the White armies.

The fight between the Whites and the Reds (December 1918 to the end of 1920)

The Red Army, based mainly in Moscow, initially soaked up attacks from the Whites from all directions. From October 1919 onwards, the Red armies scored notable victories over the Whites (for example, against General Deniken at Orel and General Yudenich at Petrograd). By the depth of winter, the Red Army had started to advance. In January 1920, Admiral Kolchak resigned (and was subsequently executed by the Bolsheviks). Certain regions, such as Ukraine, also demanded to be freed from central control, believing they should be allowed to develop a separate national identity. These regions constituted the nationalist forces that were an extra thorn in the side of the Reds. By February there were signs that the resistance from the nationalists was receding.

The war between Russia and Poland

The latter stages of the Civil War were dominated by the military conflict with Poland.

- April 1920: Polish armed forces attacked Russia and reached as far as Kiev in the east. Russian forces counter-attacked and pushed Polish troops back to Warsaw. There followed a Polish counter-attack, resulting in the retreat of the Red Army.
- October 1920: The Russo-Polish conflict eventually came to a halt with an armistice in October 1920 and the Treaty of Riga was signed in March 1921.
- November 1921: Red forces drove out the last of the White troops from southern Russia.
- Throughout 1921 groups of armed peasants formed to oppose the Bolsheviks. They were known as the Green armies.

Spider diagram

Read the question and complete a spider diagram to identify relevant reasons. Complete the spider diagram with a sentence of explanation, then prioritise your reasons by adding numbers to each oval box – with 1 as the most important reason and 6 as the least important.

'Admiral Kolchak's self-appointment as Supreme Ruler of the White armies was the most important factor that determined the course of the Civil War in Russia from 1917 to 1921.' How far do you agree?

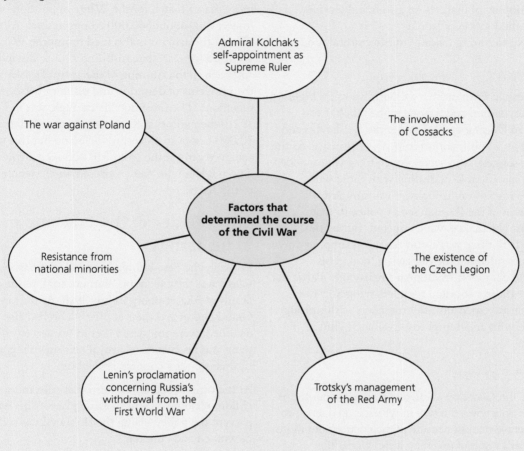

How far do you agree?

Read the following interpretation. Summarise the arguments. Use your knowledge to support and/or contradict the arguments you have identified. Record your comments using the template below.

Hint: start by thinking about the words 'almost inevitable'. When looking back at the past is it possible to argue that anything was inevitable?

'Civil war was **almost inevitable** in Russia given the Bolshevik desire to rule the whole country. They had won Petrograd but then had to consolidate their power over the largest country in the world. They wished to dispossess the previous ruling class and property owners.'

Argument in interpretation	Knowledge that supports	Knowledge that contradicts
1		
2		
3		

'War Communism'

During the Civil War, Lenin used State Capitalism alongside grain requisitioning to create what was labelled War Communism. The key features of War Communism were as follows:

- nationalisation (state control) of larger enterprises and a state monopoly of markets for goods and services
- partial militarisation of labour
- forced requisitioning (taking) of agricultural produce.

The *Cheka*

The All-Russian Extraordinary Commission for Fighting Counter-Revolution and Sabotage (the Cheka) was established in December 1917 under the Bolsheviks and was headed by a Polish communist, Dzerzhinsky. As the official title suggests, this secret police force was intended to have the specific role of dealing with those who opposed the revolution. Initially, it was similar to previous forms of the Russian secret police in that individual troublemakers were targeted. But by the summer of 1917 there was a shift towards clamping down on groups considered to be displaying 'bourgeois' elements and counter-revolutionary behaviour. Particular targets were those associated with left-wing Socialist Revolutionaries, especially after members of this group were linked with an attempt to assassinate Lenin in August 1918.

The Red Terror

What made the *Cheka* very different from previous forms of the secret police was the way in which it used terror to victimise people not just because of their actions but more generally – as a result of *who* they were. Under the guidance of Trotsky and Dzerzhinsky, the *Cheka* formally implemented the so-called Red Terror. This involved:

- enforcing War Communism (especially grain requisitioning)
- the introduction of a 'Labour Code'
- the elimination of kulaks
- the administration of Gulag labour camps
- the militarisation of labour.

The Kronstadt Rising

Under the guidance of Trotsky, the Red Army was constructed and was instrumental in enabling the Bolsheviks to win the Civil War. At the start of the war, the Red Army hardly existed but by the end it consisted of over 5 million conscripts. Such a large force proved more than a match for the White opposition, who could muster only about 500,000 troops in total. Alongside the Cheka, the army was also used to impose War Communism. Despite instilling a more disciplined approach to the running of the army, Trotsky still faced the problems of desertion and military personnel joining rebellions. The most notable example was in February 1921 when sailors at Kronstadt mutinied. Trotsky ordered 50,000 troops to recapture the island but this was achieved only at the cost of 10,000 Red Army deaths. Those rebels who were captured were executed or exiled to the Arctic.

The murder of the tsar and members of his family

Probably the best-known example of the work of the *Cheka* was the execution, without trial, of the Romanov family at Ekaterinburg in July 1918. At the same time, the Grand Dukes and their families, who had also been detained, were murdered. Lenin wanted to ensure that there was no chance of a royal heir surviving to become a figurehead for a counter-revolution.

At the time, it was announced that Alexandra and her children had been 'sent to a safe place.' This was to prevent the public seeing the Bolsheviks as ruthless killers of women and children.

Identify an argument
                  a

Below are a series of definitions, a sample exam question and two sample conclusions. One of the conclusions achieves a high mark because it contains an argument (an assertion justified with a reason). The other achieves a lower mark because it contains only description (a detailed account) and assertion (a statement of fact or an opinion which is not supported by a reason). Identify which is which. The mark scheme on page 7 will help you.

'The most important feature of the Civil War was the emergence of War Communism.' How far do you agree?

War Communism was obviously an important feature of the Civil War. Without its introduction the Bolshevik leaders would have struggled to achieve their aim of ruling the whole of Russia. War Communism provided the structure and discipline needed for the Reds to defeat their enemies. Nationalisation of key industries, the militarisation of labour and grain requisitioning all resulted in resources reaching those who needed them the most: the Red Army and producers of military hardware. However, War Communism could not have been implemented without the *Cheka*. From a Bolshevik point of view, a new type of police force was needed to ensure that the main strands of War Communism were adhered to. This was especially important as War Communism was generally disliked and opposed by the Russian people. Thus, War Communism, as policed by the *Cheka*, was the most important feature of the Civil War.

War Communism was probably the most important feature of the Civil War for three reasons. First, it involved nationalisation (state control) of larger enterprises and a state monopoly of markets for goods and services. Second, it led to the partial militarisation of labour, which was disliked as people were forced to work solely to meet the needs of the war. Third, forced requisitioning (taking) of agricultural produce occurred as a result of War Communism. This was the most hated policy, as it involved taking away surpluses of food and grain. War Communism was therefore important but there were other features of the Civil War that stood out, particularly the Red Terror.

i **You're the examiner**

Below are a sample exam question and one paragraph of an answer. Read the paragraph and the mark scheme provided on page 7. Decide which level you would award the paragraph and write a justification for your choice.

To what extent was the *Cheka* successful in helping the Bolshevik leadership achieve its aims during the Civil War?

The main aim of the Bolshevik leadership during the Civil War was to defeat the White and Green armies so that they could proceed to govern the whole of Russia. In conjunction with this, Lenin believed that he had to wipe out all traces of the old ruling regime based on property ownership. With this in mind, the *Cheka* can be seen as very successful. By the summer of 1917 it had clamped down on groups considered to be displaying 'bourgeois' elements and counter-revolutionary behaviour. What made the *Cheka* very different from previous versions of the secret police was the way in which it used terror to victimise people not just because of their actions but more generally, as a result of *who* they were. Through this approach they proved effective in enforcing the main aspects of War Communism (especially grain requisitioning).

The reasons for the Red victory

Leadership

Trotsky, acting as the Bolshevik war commissar, proved to be very skilful in managing the Red Army. No White leader matched Trotsky's strategy and tactics and his ability to sustain the morale of troops. Lenin was also instrumental in ensuring that Bolshevik supporters remained united in their belief in the socialist cause.

The White leaders struggled to co-operate and to co-ordinate their activities. This was partly due to geographical separation but also as a result of not having a common set of aims. Some Whites were socialists while others were conservatives looking to restore some kind of aristocratic rule. There were also regional differences; some White (and Green) leaders viewed the Civil War as an opportunity to seek autonomy or even independence for their region.

Strategy and tactics

Trotsky's strategy was based on maintaining lines of communication within the Red Army, breaking the supply lines to White army groups and preventing them from co-ordinating their activity.

Integral to the above strategy was the tactic of controlling and maintaining the railways, especially in the areas around Petrograd and Moscow. Trotsky and Lenin planned for links between the Red Army forces to be secured, to ensure the defence of Russia's two most important centres of industrial production, where the Bolsheviks had first consolidated their power. Once Petrograd and Moscow were deemed safe, the Red Army was then co-ordinated to go on the offensive, pushing back the White forces to the key frontlines.

The other main tactic employed by the Bolsheviks was the imposition of *Cheka* brutality (see pages 54). Without the *Cheka* it would have been difficult to impose the strict wartime measures (especially War Communism and the militarisation of labour) considered necessary for victory.

Resources

Both the Reds and the Whites used conscription to boost their forces. Trotsky turned the old Red Army of workers and peasants into a more professional and disciplined organisation. By 1920 Trotsky was managing over 3 million troops, compared with the 500,000 White soldiers estimated to have been available at any one point during the conflict. Former tsarist military officers were also employed by the Reds to counter the experience of military leaders found in the ranks of their opponents. Similarly, Red cavalry units were formed to oppose the Whites' use of Cossacks in the south. Although there were desertions from the Red Army, the Red Terror helped maintain cohesiveness.

From the start of the war the Reds controlled the industrial centres in Russia and hence were able to quickly produce munitions to support the army. In contrast, the Whites had to rely on the foreign supply of armaments.

Logistics

By controlling the railways, the Reds were able to move troops and supplies over vast distances far more quickly than the Whites. Trotsky had his own armoured train constructed so that he could move from front to front in short periods of time. He supposedly travelled over 65,000 miles during the war!

Identify the concept

Below are five sample exam questions based on some of the following concepts:

- **Cause** – questions concern the reasons for something, or why something happened
- **Consequence** – questions concern the impact of an event, an action or a policy
- **Change/continuity** – questions ask you to investigate the extent to which things changed or stayed the same
- **Similarity/difference** – questions ask you to investigate the extent to which two events, actions or policies were similar
- **Significance** – questions concern the importance of an event, an action or a policy.

Read each of the questions and work out which of the concepts they are based on.

'The weak leadership of the Whites was the main reason for the Red victory in the Civil War.' How far do you agree?

How far did the strategy and tactics of the Red Army change during the Civil War?

How important was Trotsky in enabling the Bolsheviks to succeed during the Civil War?

'The differences between the resources of the White and Red armies in the Civil War account for the Red victory.' How far do you agree?

To what extent was the Bolshevik victory in the Civil War due to the *Cheka*?

The flaw in the argument　a

Below are a sample exam question and one paragraph of an answer. The paragraph contains an argument focused on the requirements of the question. However, there is an error in the argument. Use your knowledge of this topic to identify the error.

Assess the reasons for the Bolshevik victory during the Civil War.

Probably the most important reason for the success of the Bolsheviks in the Civil War was its superior leadership. Trotsky, acting as the Bolshevik war commissar, proved to be very skilful in managing the Red Army. Some White leaders, such as Deniken, Yudenich and Kolchak, matched Trotsky's strategy and tactics and his ability to sustain the morale of troops. On the whole, though, most White leaders were ineffective. Also, the Whites had no one who could match Lenin. He was instrumental in ensuring that Bolshevik supporters remained united in their belief in the socialist cause. The White leaders struggled to co-operate and to co-ordinate their activities. This was entirely due to not having a common set of aims. The opposition to the Bolsheviks was totally dominated by Whites, who included both socialists and conservatives looking to restore some kind of aristocratic rule.

The New Economic Policy (NEP)

Motives

By 1921 workers, peasants and party members were clamouring for something 'new' to resolve the hardships caused by both the First World War and the Civil War. It is debatable as to how far Lenin viewed War Communism as a short-term emergency measure, but he was quick to change tack and replaced it with his New Economic Policy (NEP).

Content of the NEP

The key features of the NEP were as follows:

● Denationalisation of small-scale enterprise and a return to private ownership. This was to allow small workshops to flourish and produce consumer items such as clothes and shoes.
● The continuation of state control of heavy industry, but with the use of trusts. These organisations were to pay strict attention to accounting procedures and were responsible for the purchase of raw materials and equipment and the payment of wages.
● Rejuvenation of internal trade through the removal of restrictions on the private sales of goods and services. Shops flourished, rationing was ended and a new, revalued rouble was introduced.
● A return to the encouragement of external (foreign) trade and investment and the import of foreign expertise.
● An end to grain requisitioning and a return to peasants being allowed to sell surpluses in local markets.

Consequences of the NEP

The short-term impact was impressive. Industrial output increased rapidly and this was reflected in the greater amount of food and consumer goods found in shops and markets (see Table 3.2). This was linked to the emergence of a new breed of entrepreneur, the Nepman. By 1923 Nepmen were responsible for over 60 per cent of retail trade, but they had already started to annoy people with their underhand wheeling and dealing.

Another cause for concern by that time was the emergence of what Trotsky called the 'scissors crisis'. The supply of food increased at a rate that far exceeded domestic demand, resulting in a swift fall in prices. In comparison, the supply of manufactured goods increased at a much slower pace which left prices relatively high. Peasants were therefore reluctant to sell surpluses at low prices, but the frustration was that industrialists needed them to do this so that they could afford to buy their products. As the historian J.N. Westwood has pointed out, this was 'less serious than it seemed at the time' as it was only a short-term problem; the Bolshevik government quickly found a way of resolving the crisis.

▼ **Table 3.2: Russian agricultural and industrial production 1921–26.**

	1921	1922	1923	1924	1925	1926
Grain harvest (millions of tonnes)	37.6	50.3	56.6	51.4	72.5	76.8
Sown area (millions of hectares)	90.3	77.7	91.7	98.1	104.3	110.3
Industrial (factory) production (millions of roubles at 1926–27 value)	2,004	2,619	4,005	4,660	7,739	11,083
Coal (millions of tonnes)	8.9	9.5	13.7	16.1	18.1	27.6
Electricity (million of kilowatt-hours)	1,945	775	1,146	1,562	2,925	3,508
Pig iron (thousands of tonnes)	116	188	309	755	1,535	2,441
Steel (thousands of tonnes)	183	392	709	1,140	2,135	3,141
Cotton fabrics (millions of metres)	105	349	691	963	1,688	2,286
Rail freight carried (millions of tonnes)	39.4	39.9	58.0	67.5	83.4	–*

*Data not available.

Source: A. Nove, *An Economic History of the U.S.S.R.* (Allen Lane, 1969).

Delete as applicable

Below are a sample exam question and one paragraph of an answer. Read the paragraph and decide which of the possible options (in bold) is most appropriate. Delete the least appropriate options.

How successful was the New Economic Policy?

The New Economic Policy was **not/partially/very** successful insofar as it achieved **none/some/all** of its main aims (to raise production and productivity by encouraging private enterprise). The short-term impact was **negligible/impressive**. Industrial and agricultural output increased **steadily/rapidly** and this was reflected in the greater amount of food and consumer goods found in shops and markets. For example, the grain harvest went up from 37.6 tonnes in 1921 to 76.8 tonnes in 1926. This was linked to the emergence of a new breed of entrepreneur, the Nepman. By 1923 Nepmen were responsible for over 60 per cent of retail trade, **and/but** they started to **support/annoy** people with their underhand wheeling and dealing. Another cause for concern by that time was the emergence of what Trotsky called the 'Scissors Crisis'. The supply of food increased at a rate that **partly/far** exceeded domestic demand, resulting in a **slow/moderate/swift** fall in prices. In comparison, the supply of manufactured goods increased at a **much faster/moderate/slower** pace which left prices relatively high. Peasants were therefore **happy/reluctant** to sell surpluses at low prices, but the frustration was that industrialists **needed/did not need** them to do this so that they could afford to buy their products.

Support or challenge?

Below are a sample exam question which asks how far you agree with a specific statement. Below this is a series of general statements which are relevant to the question. Using your own knowledge and the information on the opposite page decide whether these statements support or challenge the statement in the question.

'The most important feature of the New Economic Policy was the stimulus given to internal trade.' How far do you agree?

Feature	Support	Challenge
Stimulus to internal trade		
Denationalisation of small-scale enterprise		
Continuation of central control of heavy industry		
Stimulus to external (foreign) trade		
An end to grain requisitioning		
Encouragement of peasants to produce and sell surpluses		

The organisation of the Bolshevik government took shape quickly after the Second All-Russian Congress of Soviets had disbanded. If the new regime had been a soviet government in the truest sense, it would have constituted a major break with the tsarist past, since genuine soviet rule would have revolved around the freedoms and liberties gained as a result of the revolts of February and March 1917. In reality, it introduced policies similar to that of the tsarist era, often in a very repressive form.

The structure and organisation of the new government

The All-Russian Congress of Soviets and the Central Executive Committee

The Congress and its organising committee (Executive Committee) was the mainstay of the new government. In the summer of 1918, the Mensheviks and SRs were expelled from the Executive Committee and it became dominated by Bolsheviks.

The Council of People's Commissars (*Sovnarkom*)

The 'people's commissars' were ministers with specific governmental responsibilities. Trotsky, for example, was placed in charge of foreign affairs. The chairman (prime minister) was Lenin. To begin with the Council also consisted of left-wing SRs. In theory, commissars were answerable to the Executive Committee.

This new system appeared to be democratic insofar as members of *Sovnarkom* were the product of a chain of elections organised by soviets at a local level. However, the soviets were dominated by the Bolshevik party, whose organisation resembled that of the new government.

The Party

The Bolshevik party was 'reshaped'.
- The Central Executive Committee of the party was responsible for the administration and operation of the key political offices: the Politburo and the Orgburo.
- The Bolsheviks promoted the party as working to create an egalitarian society based on democratic centralism. Central control of Russian affairs would be in the hands of politicians elected by the Russian people (that is, the people of the RSFSR).
- However, all the key government posts were held by senior Bolsheviks, and the administration was swamped with the 'leading cadres' of the Bolshevik Party.
- Membership numbers grew significantly during the immediate post-Civil War period. In 1921, there were around 730,000 members, but by 1928 this had increased to about a million.
- As the party and government became more centralised and nepotistic, the political regime became less democratic. Recruitment campaigns such as the Lenin Enrolment attempted to address the issue of underrepresentation of peasants and workers, but they had minimal effect on the composition of the party.

The constitutions

Two constitutions were established before the rule of Stalin.
- 1918 – this created the RSFSR (that is, Russia, but also including parts of central Asia, most notably Kazakhstan, Uzbekistan and Turkmenia).
- 1924 – this created the Federal Union of Soviet Socialist Republics (USSR). By this time, via a treaty of 1922, the Republics of Ukraine, Belarus and Transcaucasia (containing Azerbaijan, Armenia and Georgia) had joined with the RSFSR. Each republic was allowed its own government and other symbols of sovereignty such as national flags. However, such governments were still answerable to *Sovnarkom*.

Simple essay style

Below is a sample exam question. Use your own knowledge and the information on the opposite page to produce a plan for this question. Choose four general points, and provide three pieces of specific information to support each general point.

Once you have planned your essay, write the introduction and conclusion for the essay. The introduction should list the points to be discussed in the essay. The conclusion should summarise the key points and justify which point was the most important.

'The most important development in Russian government from 1917 to 1924 was the creation of *Sovnarkom*.' How far do you agree?

 ## Eliminate irrelevance

Below are a sample exam question and one paragraph of an answer. Read the paragraph and identify parts of it that are not directly relevant to the question. Draw a line through the information that is irrelevant and justify your deletions in the margin.

How effectively was Russia governed from 1917 to 1924?

The All-Russian Congress of Soviets and the Central Executive Committee were extremely important in enabling Russia to be governed effectively from 1917 to 1924. After the Second All-Russian Congress of Soviets had disbanded at the end of 1917, the shape of the new Russian government fell into place. The Congress had given the Bolsheviks a mandate to rule Russia based on the assumption that a Bolshevik government was, in the truest sense, a soviet one. If this had been the case, the new regime would have constituted a major break with the tsarist past as genuine soviet rule would have revolved around the freedoms and liberties gained as a result of the revolts of February 1917. This would have given the Bolsheviks a firm base from which to govern effectively. The Congress and its organising committee (Executive Committee) were meant to be the mainstay of the new government. In theory, the commissars were answerable to the Executive Committee, although the reality was different. When, in the summer of 1918, Mensheviks and SRs were expelled from the Executive Committee, it became dominated by Bolsheviks. Many of these were also 'people's commissars' and Russia was not far off being ruled as a 'one-party state'. The Council of People's Commissars (*Sovnarkom*) consisted of ministers who had specific governmental responsibilities. Trotsky, for example, was placed in charge of foreign affairs and Stalin had to deal with nationalities. The chairman (prime minister) was Lenin. To begin with, the Council also consisted of left-wing SRs.

The strengths and weaknesses of Lenin as leader of the Bolsheviks

How Lenin's strengths and weaknesses are viewed is likely to depend on how sympathetic one might be to what he was trying to achieve and how he went about fulfilling his aims. Also, Lenin had different strengths and weaknesses according to the role he played – as a member of the intelligentsia, party leader or leader of Russia.

Strengths

- Lenin was a 'conviction' politician. Throughout his career he stuck to his belief that the imposition of Marxist ideas was the only way for a more just, fair and equal society to come about in Russia.
- Despite his Marxist convictions, Lenin was also flexible in his thoughts and actions. For example, he initially believed that a revolution in Russia could only be achieved with the support of workers and not peasants. When peasants started to show 'revolutionary behaviour', such as seizing land from the nobility, Lenin changed his mind and acknowledged that rural protesters had an important role to play in political change (see page 40).
- Lenin's self-belief proved invaluable in helping him deal with opposition.
- When Lenin experienced setbacks, such as being exiled, he saw these as opportunities rather than threats.
- Fellow Bolsheviks displayed much loyalty towards their leader, even when they disagreed with him.
- Lenin was an opportunist; he knew when to take advantage of the weaknesses shown by his opponents, especially the Mensheviks and the Provisional Government.
- Above all, Lenin was a person of great intellect. He was adept at converting some of the more abstract ideas of Marxism into something that could be understood by workers and peasants. In response to the context he found himself working in, he developed his own ideology of Marxism–Leninism.

Weaknesses

- Lenin was not afraid to use force, with the resultant human casualties, if it meant he was to achieve his aims. Generally, Lenin could be seen as an oppressor much like the tsars (like Stalin, he has been referred to as a 'Red Tsar').
- Lenin was so single-minded about Marxism that he refused to accept that there were possible alternatives to achieving a more just society. This caused opposition, including within his own party.
- Opposition to Lenin also strengthened when he banned other political parties.
- Lenin's economic, social and political reforms could be seen to have sent Russia backwards, but much depends on how the costs and benefits of capitalism are viewed, as opposed to those of Communism.

Spectrum of importance

Below are a sample exam question and a list of general points which could be used to answer the question. Use your own knowledge and the information on the opposite page to reach a judgement about the importance of these general points to the question posed. Write numbers on the spectrum below to indicate their relative importance. Having done this, write a brief justification of your placement, explaining why some of these factors are more important than others. The resulting diagram could form the basis of an essay plan.

> To what extent was Lenin's success as the leader of the Bolsheviks due to his determination to defeat opposition?

1 Determination to defeat opposition

2 Reputation as a 'conviction' politician

3 Adherence to Marxist ideology

4 Opportunism

5 Ability to gain loyalty and respect from other Bolsheviks

6 Great intellect

← ─────────────────────────────────────── →

Least important   Most important

 Recommended reading

Below is a list of suggested further reading on this topic.
- Vladimir Ilich Lenin, *The State and Revolution* (Martino Fine Books, 2011)
- Michael Lynch, *Russia 1894-1941*, Chapter 5 (Hodder 2015)
- Christopher Read, *Lenin* (Routledge, 2005)
- John Reed, *Ten Days that Shook the World* (Penguin, 2007)
- Robert Service, *Lenin: A Biography* (Macmillan, 2000)

Exam focus

Below is a sample of a higher-level answer to an AS and A-Level-style essay question. Read the answer and the comments around it.

'The weaknesses of their enemies were the main reasons for the Bolshevik victory in the Russia Civil War.' How far do you agree?

After taking control of Russia from the Provisional Government, the Bolsheviks under Lenin moved on to consolidate power. A peace was negotiated with Germany to end Russia's involvement in the First World War, but the Bolsheviks soon found themselves embroiled in another military conflict, a Civil War. It is possible that Lenin wanted the Civil War to occur, as it gave him the opportunity to wipe out his opponents. By the end of the war he had achieved his aim. It seems clear that the Bolsheviks' enemies (known as the Whites) displayed weaknesses, with respect to clear objectives, leadership, strategy, tactics, resources and logistics, which help explain the Bolshevik victory. However, these should not be overemphasised, as the Bolsheviks displayed much strength in the same areas where their opponents displayed their shortcomings.

With respect to objectives, the Whites had a variety of aims depending on their political ideologies. Some Whites were socialists while others were conservatives looking to restore some kind of aristocratic rule. There were also regional differences; some White (and Green) leaders viewed the Civil War as an opportunity to seek autonomy or even independence for their region. The military leaders of the Whites also had personal ambitions to gain power and appeared wary of co-ordinating their activities. The Bolsheviks, on the other hand, had an overriding objective, which was to defeat their enemies to ensure that communism could be installed throughout Russia. Having a single objective helped Lenin and Trotsky to bind their support.

Objectives were obviously linked to the quality of leadership. As indicated above, no one person was in charge of the White forces. The Whites had many rival figures, such as Yudenich, Wrangel, Kolchak and Denikin, vying for control in particular geographical areas. They were all ambitious and each was determined to eventually gain leadership of Russia for himself. As a result, there was virtually no co-operation between the various White armies – they fought independently, making it easier for the Red Army to defeat them individually. In contrast, Trotsky, acting as the Bolshevik war commissar, proved to be very skilful in managing the Red Army. No White leader matched Trotsky's strategy and tactics and his ability to sustain the morale of troops. Trotsky also imposed a very tough system of discipline and control over the Red Army. Officers found guilty of cowardice or treachery were executed, whereas men who showed initiative and courage were promoted rapidly. At times of crisis, Trotsky readily assumed personal command of areas under threat, inspiring and encouraging the troops to greater efforts and eventual victory. Lenin was also key in ensuring that Bolshevik supporters remained united in their belief in the socialist cause. He had managed the Bolsheviks to victory in the October Revolution. Throughout the Civil War, Lenin provided the energy and commitment needed to inspire success. At all times, he had very definite aims and objectives and a sense of purpose (unlike his opponents) about what he believed was best for Russia. His leadership was never challenged.

The issue of different objectives and leadership skills resulted in the Whites having no clear strategy or tactics to win the war. This was probably their most important weakness: without a co-ordinated plan the White armies were easy to pick off. Trotsky's strategy was based on keeping open lines of communication within the Red Army, destroying the supply lines to White army groups and stopping them from co-ordinating their activity. Connected to this was the tactic of controlling and maintaining the railways, especially in the areas around Petrograd and Moscow. Trotsky and Lenin planned for links between the Red Army forces to

This is a solid introduction that provides a contextual setting and indicates the line of argument to be taken (White weaknesses in a number of areas but to be compared with Bolshevik strengths).

The answer starts with a factor (objectives) which is explained and analysed. A comparative approach has been adopted, which allows for evaluation of the factor and adds to the clear structure of the essay.

The comparative approach is continued in this paragraph; the leadership issue is well developed, although it may have benefited from the inclusion of more precise support material.

This paragraph shows more explanation – so far there is very little description or illustration of what happened. The focus remains tightly on the question set.

Quick quizzes at **www.hoddereducation.co.uk/myrevisionnotes**

be secured first, to ensure the defence of Russia's two most important centres of industrial production, where the Bolsheviks had first consolidated their power. Once Petrograd and Moscow were deemed safe, the Red Army was then co-ordinated to go on the offensive, pushing back the White forces to the key frontlines.

The Whites used brutality as a tactic to maintain discipline, gain support and boost resources. This was done in a fairly arbitrary way and, as a result, was detested. In areas they controlled, towns and villages were ransacked and set fire to. Property was requisitioned, including peasant farmers' crops and livestock. If people objected, they faced torture and execution. The Whites lost support from rural areas in particular, and peasant groups (Greens) formed to resist but also to form alliances with the Bolsheviks. In comparison, the Bolsheviks also deployed force as a tactic but in a more organised way. The *Cheka* (secret police) was formed to impose strict wartime measures (especially War Communism and the militarisation of labour) and to seek out the opponents of the Bolsheviks. The emergence of the so-called Red Terror was a planned and consistently implemented strategy, unlike the unplanned, more random use of violence used by the Whites.

> This section continues with the factor-based approach and the answer remains focused.

The Bolsheviks organised a highly effective propaganda campaign in the areas they controlled. Through speeches, newspapers, and leaflets, people were continually told that the Bolsheviks were now in charge of Russia through the soviets, that life would be better and that wealth would be distributed more fairly. In addition, they were told that the White armies and their leaders would destroy all the achievements of the Revolution, break up the soviets and bring back the old system. In this way, support for the Bolsheviks was organised and built up successfully.

> A rather thin paragraph, but it does contain explanation with a hint of judgement about the factor at the end.

As the White forces were geographically dispersed and not located near to densely populated areas, it was difficult for them to boost their resources. The Bolsheviks, on the other hand, controlled the major cities from the start, which provided fresh recruitment for the Red Army. Furthermore, much of Russia's industry and raw material was situated in such cities. It was relatively easy, therefore, for the Bolsheviks to keep their troops supplied and equipped with weapons, ammunition, uniforms and food. Both the Whites and the Reds used conscription to boost their forces, but the Bolsheviks appeared better at doing this. Trotsky turned the old Red Army of workers and peasants into a more professional and disciplined organisation. By 1920 Trotsky was managing over 3 million troops, compared with the 500,000 White soldiers that were estimated to be available at any one point during the conflict. Former tsarist military officers were also employed by the Reds to counter the experience of military leaders found in the ranks of their opponents. Similarly, Red cavalry units were formed to oppose the Whites' use of Cossacks in the south. There were desertions from the Red Army, but the Red Terror helped maintain cohesiveness. From the start of the war the Reds controlled the industrial centres in Russia and hence were able to quickly produce munitions to support the army. In contrast, the Whites had to rely on the foreign supply of armaments, which proved unreliable. The weakness of not having comparable resources was very significant; even if the Whites had had good leadership skills and a carefully planned strategy, they would still have struggled without appropriate numbers of men and armaments.

> A rather long section but it contains a well-developed analysis of the resource issue with a clear interim judgement at the end.

With respect to logistics, the sheer size of Russia worked against the White armies. They had to move their forces and supplies over huge distances, making it difficult to maintain effective control. The lack of effective railways was an added complication to the existing communication difficulties between them. By controlling the railways the Reds were able to move troops and supplies over vast distances far more quickly than the Whites. Trotsky had his own armoured train constructed so that he could move from front to front in short periods of time. He supposedly travelled over 65,000 miles during the war. This illustrates the importance the Reds placed on accessing the railway network.

In conclusion, the enemies of the Bolsheviks clearly showed relative weaknesses in all of the key areas of warfare. Most of their shortcomings were linked to a lack of common purpose and, hence, a lack of co-ordination of their efforts. However, the Bolsheviks still had to exploit these weaknesses to ensure victory. It was the determination, skill and intellect of both Lenin and Trotsky that led to the Bolshevik triumph. Without their contributions, the Bolsheviks would have struggled to utilise the advantages in strategy, logistics or resources that they appeared to have from the start.

> The conclusion makes a clear judgement linked to the factors discussed in the main body of the answer and to the question. Without this, the answer may not have achieved a mark in the highest level, as interim judgements are somewhat lacking.

This answer would reach a high level at both AS and A-Level. There is consistent focus on the key factor in the question (White weaknesses) and how this compares with another factor (Red strengths) with respect to importance. The candidate uses a range of themes to structure their answer. Each theme is explained, supported and analysed, and ends with an interim judgement.

Exam focus

REVISED ☐

Below is a sample of a higher-level answer to an AS-style interpretations question. Read the answer and the comments around it.

'The NEP was a compromise that postponed into the future any form of collective ownership of land or of produce.'

From: S. Lee, *Russia and the USSR, 1855–1991,* 2006

Evaluate the strengths and limitations of this interpretation, making reference to other interpretations that you have studied.

> In this opening paragraph, the interpretation is explained and initially assessed with reference to different ways in which the NEP can be viewed.

The interpretation carries some weight in that the New Economic Policy (NEP) could be viewed as a compromise; it put an end to grain requisitioning and allowed peasants to sell surpluses in local markets while giving the Bolsheviks time to prepare for a move towards collectivisation. However, the interpretation ignores the fact that the NEP might also be considered as representing a reward to peasants and workers for their support during the Civil War. Another view worth considering is that the NEP was not just about improving the position of rural folk but was also aimed at boosting the living standards of the urban population.

> This paragraph uses contextual knowledge to evaluate the interpretation (at the start and end). The evaluation is clearly stated and linked to the interpretation, not simply implied.

The main implication of the interpretation is that the NEP was introduced as a means to win over the rural population before there was a move back to a more communal way of farming. This emphasises the strength of the interpretation, as the ending of grain requisitioning certainly pleased farmers and the move to allow surpluses to be sold in markets appeared to lead to the creation of a new, wealthier class of peasants called *kulaks*. As a result of a more motivated rural workforce, the grain harvest rose from about 38 million tonnes in 1921 to about 56 million tonnes in 1923. There was more food available for urban dwellers and for export, which helped boost the Russian economy more generally. However, this effect of the NEP would appear to invalidate the interpretation in some ways. It seems strange that the NEP could be considered only a short-term measure, to be replaced by collectivisation, when it had such positive and dramatic results.

> This paragraph provides balanced analysis of the interpretation by offering an alternative view of the NEP. It is consistent in linking the evaluation directly to the question.

The stress that the interpretation places on the NEP being a compromise also has some validity. Peasants, in particular, had suffered considerably during the Civil War as a result of War Communism, the use of the *Cheka* to requisition grain and the brutality of the Whites. The NEP would seem to have been a kind of reward for putting up with such hardships and displaying loyalty to the Bolshevik cause. In return, the Bolsheviks would have hoped that peasant support for communism would have strengthened. However, the interpretation also falls down in this respect, as it suggests that the Bolsheviks were simply using the NEP as a sweetener for what was to come. It could be that when the NEP was first introduced Lenin sincerely believed it was the most appropriate way for the Russian economy to develop. The fact that the 'leftists' opposed the NEP, as they believed it betrayed the revolution, suggests that Lenin did not promote his policy as a short-term fix. It was only when Stalin came to power that there was a full reversal of the NEP. This would appear to weaken the interpretation considerably.

Furthermore, the interpretation is rather weak in that it focuses on rural issues and ignores the stimuli that the NEP was designed to give to trade and industry. Other interpretations stress how the NEP provided for a return to private ownership of industrial production. Small workshops were allowed to flourish, to produce consumer items such as clothes and shoes. Although there was continuation of state control of heavy industry, this was done through the creation of trusts. These organisations were to pay strict attention to accounting procedures and were responsible for the purchase of raw materials and equipment and the payment of wages. There was also a rejuvenation of internal trade through the removal of restrictions on the private sales of goods and services. Shops proliferated, rationing was ended and a new, revalued rouble was introduced. A return to the encouragement of external (foreign) trade, investment and the import of foreign expertise occurred. All of this suggests that the NEP was not, as the interpretation suggests, focused simply on appeasing peasants before getting them to accept collectivisation. The interpretation shows another weakness, therefore, by adopting such a narrow focus on the motives behind the NEP.

> The evaluation of the interpretation continues in the same way as in the previous paragraphs. It is balanced, coherent and uses an alternative viewpoint to reveal a weakness of the interpretation.

Finally, the fact that Stalin did introduce collectivisation strengthens the validity of the interpretation. It implies that 'giving peasants their little bit of capitalism' was considered to be short term. But there is an argument that suggests Stalin's overturning of the NEP was connected to the emergence of the 'scissors crisis'. Trotsky observed that, after the introduction of the NEP, the supply of food increased at a rate that far exceeded domestic demand. The result was a sharp fall in prices. In comparison, the supply of manufactured goods increased at a much slower pace, which left prices of such goods relatively high. Peasants were obviously not keen to sell surpluses at lower prices. The problem was that industrialists needed them to do this, so that consumers could afford to buy their products. To avert unrest and a challenge to Stalin's authority (especially from 'rightists') it might be that the Russian leader felt the need to bring back an element of control over agricultural production. Thus, the NEP was not so much of a compromise, as the interpretation suggests, but more of positive step to boost the economy that eventually went wrong.

> Again, the answer offers an alternative interpretation based on contextual knowledge to reveal a weakness in the view put forward by Lee.

To conclude, the interpretation on balance reveals more weaknesses than strengths as a view about the importance of the NEP. In particular, the focus on collectivisation means that the interpretation misses the important point about the overall aim of the NEP, which was to develop the Russian economy.

> Interpretation questions do not require candidates to make overall judgements in a conclusion. However, it is a neat way of completing the evaluation.

This shows an excellent understanding of the debate and how the given interpretation fits into the wider discussions about the importance of the NEP. The interpretation is clearly evaluated and analysed through comparison with detailed own knowledge. The response evaluates both the strengths and weaknesses of the interpretation. It is clearly a high-quality answer that would reach a high level.

4 The rule of Stalin

The character and abilities of Stalin REVISED

Character

Stalin is often depicted as a schemer and obsessive in wanting to gain personal power. His megalomania seems to have gone hand-in-hand with psychopathic tendencies, especially later in his career when he instigated the Great Terror. This was fuelled by a level of paranoia; Stalin increasingly believed that no one was to be trusted, including loyal party supporters and members of his own family.

However, the view of Stalin as a madman has recently been challenged by the historian Stephen Kotkin. He believes that Stalin was far more diligent, intelligent, resourceful and rational than has often been made out.

Abilities

Stalin had many abilities as a Bolshevik party member and, later in his life, as leader of communist Russia. He was a competent administrator, manager and planner of strategy and resources. As General Secretary of the Communist Party (1922) and leader of Russia, Stalin showed he could manipulate situations to serve his wants and needs. His aims were not simply based on selfishness; they can be viewed as an attempt to modernise Russia from within, while protecting it from external threats.

Stalin as an administrator

The following are examples of how able Stalin could be in these areas:

- In 1905 Stalin emerged to represent local branches of the Bolshevik Party (Georgia and South Russia) at conferences.
- In 1912 Stalin was elected to the Central Committee of the Bolsheviks where he excelled as an administrator and debater.

Stalin as a manager

Stalin was given extra responsibilities after showing his skill as a member of the Central Committee.

- From 1917 to 1922 Stalin was the Bolsheviks' specialist manager of national minorities' issues (having been appointed Commissar for Nationalities in the first Soviet government).
- Stalin's management skills were also evident in the role he played as a commander during the Civil War.
- As General Secretary of the Communist Party (1922) Stalin held the most senior of all management posts.
- As a manager of people, Stalin was adept when dealing with those involved in the power struggle after Lenin's death (especially Trotsky, Kamenev and Zinoviev). By 1927 Stalin controlled the Party Congress, which allowed him to expel his main rivals from the party.
- Stalin's more sinister management of people can be seen through the instigation of the Great Terror and show trials (1936–38) and the appointment of Beria as head of the secret police (see page 74).
- From 1939 to 1941, Stalin managed Russia's resources to prepare for a possible Nazi invasion.

Stalin as a planner

Stalin planned economic and social change, linking this with target-setting, in an attempt to modernise Russia and improve its standing as a world power. This was reflected in:

- the introduction, from 1928 to 1933, of a planned economy and the police state; in 1928 the first Five-Year Plan was adopted
- the start of the collectivisation programme in 1928.

By January 1924 Stalin had worked himself into a position of power, based on his experience of holding senior political posts. He could not have reached this position through luck. He had the ability to plan, organise, and implement his ideas effectively. This was revealed in the way he became leader of Russia and in how he implemented his plans to modernise Russia.

However, Stalin also had the ability to be ruthless when he deemed it necessary. He used an unprecedented level of repression when faced with what appeared to be intractable issues such as Lenin's legacy, a stagnant economy, opposition from national minorities and a changing world political climate.

Support your judgement

Below are a sample exam question and two basic judgements. Read the exam question and the two judgements. Support the judgement that you agree with more strongly by adding a reason that justifies the judgement.

'The Great Terror revealed that Stalin was, above all, a paranoid psychopath.' How far do you agree?

Overall, Stalin's adoption of the Great Terror did reveal that he was mainly concerned with eliminating imagined opposition.

_____

_____

Although Stalin did show psychopathic tendencies in dealing with opposition, he also revealed that he could be diligent, smart and resourceful in dealing with the challenges he faced.

_____

_____

Tip: Whichever option you choose, you will have to weigh up both sides of the argument. You could use phrases such as 'whereas' or words like 'although' in order to help the process of evaluation.

Establish criteria

Below is a sample exam question which requires you to make a judgement. The key term in the question has been marked in bold. Defining the meaning of the key term can help you establish criteria that you can use to make a judgement.

Read the question, define the key term and then set out two or three criteria based on the key term, which you can use to reach and justify a judgement. You should also use the mark scheme on page 7 to help you with this.

'Stalin showed great ability in **improving** the Russian economy.' How far do you agree?

Definition:

_____

_____

Criteria to judge the extent to which Stalin showed the ability to improve the Russian economy:

_____

_____

_____

_____

Rivals

During Lenin's stewardship, there were a number of occasions when internal disagreement threatened to derail the revolutionary movement:

- After the overthrow of the Provisional Government in 1917, a number of prominent Bolsheviks, including Kamenev, Zinoviev and Rykov, called for a coalition to be formed with other socialist groups. Although some left-wing SRs were allowed to join the ranks, Lenin bullied his Bolshevik colleagues into rejecting an alliance with opposing political groups.
- The signing of the Treaty of Brest-Litovsk was opposed by the left, especially Trotsky. Lenin countered his opponents by claiming the war would soon be over.
- The adoption of War Communism (see page 54) during the Civil War was considered harsh by some party members. Lenin conceded to pressure for change and introduced his New Economic Policy (NEP) (see page 58). This heightened tensions and widened divisions. Right-wing Bolsheviks favoured this temporary concession towards capitalism, while left-wing Bolsheviks saw it as a betrayal of revolutionary principles.

The ideological battle: 'socialism in one country' versus 'permanent revolution'

After Lenin's death, a certain amount of manoeuvring for power occurred, which highlighted the factions that still existed within the party. Leading Bolsheviks disagreed over three key issues:

- Firstly, there was much dispute between left-and right-wing Bolsheviks over whether there should be a continuation of the NEP.
- Secondly, many demanded that a more openly democratic form of government should be adopted.
- Finally, the link between ideology and the future of communism caused much consternation. The left, under the guidance of Trotsky, continued to press for a Permanent Revolution, while the right emphasised the need for socialism in one country.

Strategy and tactics

Stalin displayed skill in manipulating debates and individuals to consolidate his position, and thereby paving the way for a personal dictatorship. He also gave validation to his credentials as overall leader by obtaining important positions in the Bolshevik party earlier in his career.

Stalin's split with Zinoviev and Kamenev

The *Troika* (Stalin, Kamenev and Zinoviev) successfully discredited Trotsky, who was replaced as Commissar for War in January 1925. However, Kamenev and Zinoviev became concerned by Stalin's plan for dealing with peasants and his foreign policy. They turned on Stalin, but with little success; both were removed as secretaries of their local party. The Politburo was simultaneously expanded (from six to eight members) and reinforced with Stalinists.

The United Opposition group

Trotsky, Kamenev and Zinoviev responded by forming the United Opposition group. Their opposition to the NEP and demands for more 'free speech' were treated with contempt. All were excluded from the Politburo. By 1927 Trotsky was expelled from the party, and after continuing to provoke trouble was exiled to Kazakhstan. In January 1929 he was expelled from the USSR altogether.

The proposals for collectivisation

Stalin's proposals for collectivisation, including renewed grain requisitioning, were opposed by those on the right, who thought it resembled aspects of War Communism. Bukharin was particularly vocal in expressing his concerns and, as a result of joining forces with Kamenev, was branded a Factionalist.

The removal of Bukharin

In 1929 Bukharin was ousted from his positions as President of Comintern, editor of *Pravda* and member of the Politburo. Tomsky and Rykov also suffered demotions. Stalin simply gained the agreement of a core of loyal party members in order to remove 'critics' from positions of power. With both the left and the right removed from key jobs, Stalin was free to dominate government.

! Spot the mistake

Below are a sample exam question and one paragraph of an answer. Why does this paragraph not get high praise? What is wrong with the focus of the answer in this paragraph?

'Divisions in the Bolshevik party from 1917 to 1929 were the result of ideological differences.' How far do you agree?

During Lenin's leadership, there were a number of occasions when divisions in the party threatened to derail the revolutionary movement. These divisions were partly due to ideological differences. Disagreements first became apparent after the overthrow of the Provisional Government in 1917, when a number of prominent Bolsheviks, including Kamenev, Zinoviev and Rykov, called for a coalition to be formed with other socialist groups. Although some left-wing SRs were allowed to join ranks, Lenin bullied his Bolshevik colleagues into rejecting an alliance with opposing political groups, as they had completely different ideologies. After Lenin's death in 1924, a certain amount of manoeuvring for power occurred, which highlighted the factions that still existed within the party. Leading Bolsheviks disagreed over three key issues, all of which were linked to conflicting ideologies. First, there was much dispute between left- and right-wing Bolsheviks over whether there should be a continuation of the NEP. The left wanted to maintain the NEP whereas the right wanted to scrap it, as they considered it to be bourgeois. Second, many Bolsheviks demanded that a more openly democratic form of government should be adopted. Finally, the link between ideology and the future of communism caused much consternation. The left, under the guidance of Stalin, continued to press for a Permanent Revolution while the right, led by Trotsky, emphasised the need for socialism in one country.

! Complete the paragraph

Below are a sample exam question and one paragraph of an answer. The paragraph contains a point and specific examples, but lacks a concluding analytical link back to the question. Complete the paragraph, adding this link back to the question in the space provided.

To what extent did Stalin gain power as a result of the weakness of his opponents?

It is reasonable to argue that those who opposed Stalin were relatively weak. For example, when Kamenev and Zinoviev became concerned by Stalin's plan for dealing with peasants and his foreign policy they turned against him, but with little success; both were removed as secretaries of their local party. Furthermore, the Politburo was simultaneously expanded (from six to eight members) and reinforced with Stalinists. Trotsky, Kamenev and Zinoviev responded by forming the United Opposition group. However, their opposition to the NEP and demands for more 'free speech' were treated with contempt by Stalin and his supporters. All were excluded from the Politburo. By 1927 Trotsky was expelled from the party and, after continuing to provoke trouble, he was exiled to Kazakhstan. In January 1929 he was expelled from the USSR altogether. Another opponent, Bukharin, was ousted from his position as President of Comintern, editor of Pravda and member of the Politburo. Tomsky and Rykov also suffered demotions. Stalin gained the agreement of a core of loyal party members in order to remove 'critics' from positions of power. Overall,

_____

_____

Stalin's tactics and victory: consolidation of power through propaganda and censorship

The use of propaganda was closely linked to censorship. Stalin was something of a master in the use of both.

Propaganda under Stalin

The use of slogans

The Bolsheviks were adept at using slogans to communicate their message to the population, such as 'Peace, Bread and Land' and 'All Power to the Soviets'. Just like the tsarists, they also used pamphlets, tracts, newspapers, photographs, portraits, posters and statues.

The cult of personality

Stalin promoted a cult of personality in which he was to be worshipped as a hero. Examples of this cult included:

- the renaming of Tsaritsyn as Stalingrad (1923)
- the slogan 'Stalin is the Lenin of Today' (1924)
- various posters, photographs and statues depicting Stalin as a man of the people (usually dressed as a peasant).

Newspapers

Under the communists, the main newspapers, *Pravda* and *Izvestiia*, were primarily propaganda tools. Stalin used them effectively to promote the achievements of the Five-Year Plans.

Groups

Special youth organisations were established (the Pioneers and *Komsomol*) to protect the young against the 'degeneracy of bourgeois culture'. *Komsomol* members were encouraged to tell tales on those who criticised their leaders. Membership increased fivefold from 1929 to 1941.

The arts

The arts were manipulated to present a popular culture that emphasised the role of the 'little man', and traditional values. This was especially evident, early on in the Stalinist era, in the work of the Society of Easel Painters which included Moscow artists such as Aleksandr Deyneka, Yuri Pimanov, Aleksandr Labas and Pyotr Vilyams. Any trends that veered from the norm, such as jazz music, were banned.

The Stakhanovite movement

Propaganda was used in the workplace to raise productivity. The best example of this was the creation of the Stakhanovite movement. This was based on the extraordinary efforts of the Donbas miner, Alexei Stakhanov, who produced far above the normal quantity of coal per shift. He was turned into a 'model' worker for others to copy. Those who succeeded were given special rewards, such as red carpets and holidays in Moscow.

Leisure

Leisure pursuits were also targeted to promote communist ideals, and the Dynamo and Spartak Moscow football teams were used to show the rest of Europe how successfully Russian people could perform under Communist rule.

The use of film and the cinema to promote Communism

By the late 1920s Stalin was using the cinema to promote collectivisation and his Five-Year Plans. Under the guidance of the Council of People's Commissars, Soviet cinema was immersed in 'socialist realism' (the 'official' way of representing, through writing and the visual arts, the heroic efforts of workers and peasants, to ensure the success of communism).

Censorship under Stalin

Under Stalin, censorship was increased. By 1932 all literary groups were closed down and anyone wanting to write had to join the Union of Soviet Writers (USW). During the first congress of the group in 1934, it was announced that members had to produce material under the banner of 'socialist realism'. This involved writing to depict the struggle of ordinary people to overcome oppression.

The Second World War and the New Soviet Man

A high degree of censorship continued throughout and after the Second World War. Stalin was especially concerned with doctoring information about the rest of the world. Radio airways were distorted, news reports were fictionalised and restrictions were put on all of the arts to prevent 'bourgeois' behaviour. Writers were still valued highly as the 'engineers of men's souls' (according to Stalin) but only if they focused on glorifying Russia's achievements and promoted the concept of the New Soviet Man – that is, the ideal Soviet citizen, hard-working, law-abiding, moral and supportive of the Communist Party.

Identify the concept

Below are five sample exam questions based on some of the following concepts:
- **Cause** – questions concern the reasons for something, or why something happened
- **Consequence** – questions concern the impact of an event, an action or a policy
- **Change/continuity** – questions ask you to investigate the extent to which things changed or stayed the same
- **Similarity/difference** – questions ask you to investigate the extent to which two events, actions or policies were similar
- **Significance** – questions concern the importance of an event, an action or a policy.

Read each of the questions and work out which of the concepts they are based on.

'Stalin used propaganda mainly to promote how great the Soviet Union had become.' How far do you agree?

How important was the cult of personality in enabling Stalin to consolidate power?

'Stalin's use of censorship had a much greater impact than his use of propaganda in enabling him to maintain power.' How far do you agree?

To what extent did Stalin's use of propaganda and censorship change from 1923 to 1941?

'There was little difference in the tools of propaganda used by Stalin: they all revolved around the use of the written word.' How far do you agree?

Identify key terms

Below is a sample question which includes a key word and/or term. Key terms are important because their meaning can be helpful in structuring your answer, developing an argument, and establishing criteria that will help form the basis of a judgement.

'Propaganda was the most powerful tool used by Stalin in helping him consolidate power.' How far do you agree?

- First, identify the key word or term. This will be a word or phrase that is important to the meaning of the question. Underline the word or phrase.
- Secondly, define the key phrase. Your definition should set out the key features of the phrase or word that you are defining.
- Third, make an essay plan that reflects your definition.
- Finally, write a sentence answering the question that refers back to the definition.

Now repeat the task and consider how the change in key terms affects the structure, argument and final judgement of your essay.

'Propaganda was a powerful tool used by Stalin in helping him gain power.' How far do you agree?

Stalin's tactics and victory: consolidation of power through repression

The growth of the police state

OGPU

Once the Civil War was over, the Bolsheviks saw the need to improve their somewhat tarnished image, which meant getting rid of the *Cheka*. It was disbanded by Kamenev in 1922 and replaced by the State Police Administration (GPU). The latter was expanded in 1924 and renamed the United State Police Administration (OGPU). Although OGPU was not as brutal as the *Cheka*, it was still the secret police and therefore maintained a presence that instilled fear in the general populace. It was also entirely under the control of the Communist Party of the Soviet Union (CPSU).

NKVD

To combat opposition to Stalin's personal dictatorship, the NKVD (the People's Commissariat for Internal Affairs) was established in 1934. Headed by Yagoda (and later Yezhov), the NKVD created a permanent form of terror. It was crucial to the imposition of purges, and was notable for gathering evidence against high-rank communists such as Bukharin, Kamenev, Zinoviev and Trotsky.

However, Stalin suspected the NKVD of conspiracy. In 1938, Yezhov was blamed for an anti-purge campaign. He was replaced by Beria, who proceeded to arrange the execution of Yezhov and his close allies. By the start of the Second World War, the NKVD itself had been purged of around 20,000 members.

Show trials

These were public trials of Stalin's political rivals (Lenin had used a similar 'tool'). Individuals were 'persuaded' to admit to their crimes in front of a large audience before being sentenced (usually to death). Under Stalin there were three important show trials, in 1936, 1937 and 1938.

Purges

Throughout the 1930s, there was a change of policy: critics ceased to be removed from key political posts, and were instead removed from the party altogether. According to the historian J.N. Westwood, purging involved the 'weeding out from party membership of those characters deemed unfit through ... arbitrary arrests, fake trials, mass executions, and forced labour camps'. The purges of the 1930s were characterised as follows:

- Party members who failed to implement collectivisation adequately, or who disagreed with Stalin's attempt to 'liquidate the kulaks as a class', lost their party card, reducing total membership by about a tenth.
- During the mid-1930s, the party shed a further one-third of its members, who were seen to be resisting the pace of industrialisation and collectivisation.
- From the mid-1930s, some prominent Politburo members were exiled or executed after being called oppositionists. The most notable example was Kirov, the popular secretary of the Leningrad soviet who was murdered in 1934.
- Of the 1996 delegates who attended the 1934 Party Congress, 1108 were executed within three years.
- By the beginning of the Second World War, Stalin's paranoia over those he believed to be challenging his authority receded.

Any internal opposition to Stalin was eliminated and not just displaced.

Gulags

The NKVD also helped administer the gulags; over 40 million people were sent to these prison camps during the Stalinist regime.

Establish criteria

Below is a sample exam question which requires you to make a judgement. The key term in the question has been marked in bold. Defining the meaning of the key term can help you establish criteria that you can use to make a judgement. Read the question, define the key term and then set out two or three criteria based on the key term, which you can use to reach and justify a judgement.

'The show trials were the most **effective** tool of repression used by Stalin.' How far do you agree?

Definition:

_____

_____

Criteria to judge the effectiveness of the tools of repression used by Stalin:

_____

_____

_____

_____

Reach a judgement

Having defined the key term and established a series of criteria, you should now make a judgement. Consider how far the show trials were the most effective tool of repression used by Stalin. Summarise your judgements below:

Criterion 1:

_____

Criterion 2:

_____

Criterion 3:

_____

Criterion 4:

_____

Finally, make an overall judgement. Based on the criteria, how accurate is it to say that the show trials were the most effective tool of repression used by Stalin?

_____

_____

_____

Tip: Remember that you should weigh up evidence of the effectiveness of the show trials against evidence of the use of other tools of repression.

Agricultural policies in the 1930s: collectivisation

Collectivisation refers to the process of bringing a number of small farm units together to form bigger farms. The idea was that peasants would then collaborate to produce as much food as possible to feed themselves and the growing urban proletariat. It was aimed at preventing surpluses being hoarded until they could be sold in markets at the highest possible prices (something Stalin viewed as bourgeois and anti-revolutionary).

In general, peasants opposed collectivisation. Before Stalin emerged as leader of Russia, only about 3 per cent of peasant farmers were working on collectives started under Lenin.

Mass collectivisation

The famine of 1927–28 prompted Stalin to push for mass collectivisation. He was more generally motivated by the wish to create 'socialism in the countryside'. In turn, this involved getting rid of the NEP, eradicating the wealthier class of peasants (the so-called *kulaks*) and marginalising 'rightists' who supported a more commercially based agricultural policy.

By March 1930 Stalin claimed that 58 per cent of all households had been collectivised, which was a gross exaggeration. Nevertheless, 'mass collectivisation' had a dramatic effect, as witnessed by widespread opposition from peasants and local officials. Stalin blamed problems with collectivisation on regional officials, who he argued had become 'intoxicated with success'.

By the end of March 1930, the pace of collectivisation slackened and Stalin coupled this with a proclamation allowing peasants to quit collectives to which they had recently signed up. This fitted in with Stalin's claim that collectivisation was voluntary. The inevitable mass exodus followed, only to be quickly clamped down on by renewed pressure to collectivise by the end of the year. Hence, collectivisation was in practice a forced process; peasants could opt out but would be threatened to conform.

Renewed collectivisation and mechanisation

The move back towards intensive collectivisation had the following results:

- About 50 per cent of all peasants were once again brought together in **kolkhozy** ('pure' collectives). By the end of 1937 the figure had increased to 93 per cent.
- In contrast to the first wave of collectives, peasants were now allowed to keep small plots of land.
- Blocks of 40 farms were organised through motor-tractor stations (MTS). As the name suggests, these were originally organisations through which tractors and other heavy equipment could be loaned to peasants. An MTS would be responsible for distributing seed, collecting grain, establishing levels of payment for produce and deciding on what produce farmers could keep for their own consumption.

The famine of 1932–34 disrupted the development of collectivisation. Partly as a result of this, a special charter was issued in 1935 to improve payments to farmers in the *kolkhozy* and to give owners of small plots more legal security. Interestingly, the small plots proved more productive than the collective farms, especially when it came to supplying dairy goods.

The impact of collectivisation

- By 1941, 98 per cent of all peasant households worked on collectives.
- In 1929 Russia produced nearly 67 million tonnes of grain, compared with about 75 million tonnes in 1939. If accurate, these figures suggest that collectivisation had a positive impact on the Russian economy; more food was produced to feed the growing urban workforce but also for export.
- Despite an improvement in conditions on collective farms they were still disliked by peasants; they were seen to have destroyed traditional farming communities, to have deprived peasants of the right to make a little extra income and to have contributed to rather than solved the problem of famines, such as that of 1932–34.

Establish criteria

Below is a sample exam question which requires you to make a judgement. The key term in the question has been marked in bold. Defining the meaning of the key term can help you establish criteria that you can use to make a judgement. Read the question, define the key term and then set out two or three criteria based on the key term, which you can use to reach and justify a judgement.

'Stalin's policy of collectivisation had a totally **negative** impact on Russian agriculture from 1929 to 1941.' How far do you agree?

Definition:

_____

_____

Criteria to judge the extent to which Stalin's policy of collectivisation had a negative impact on Russian agriculture from 1929 to 1941:

_____

_____

_____

_____

Reach a judgement

Having defined the key term and established a series of criteria, you should now make a judgement about the question ('Stalin's policy of collectivisation had a totally **negative** impact on Russian agriculture from 1929 to 1941.' How far do you agree?). Consider how far collectivisation had a negative impact on Russian agriculture from 1929 to 1941. Summarise your judgements below:

Criterion 1:

_____

Criterion 2:

_____

Criterion 3:

_____

Criterion 4:

_____

Finally, make an overall judgement. Based on the criteria, how accurate is it to say that collectivisation had a negative impact on Russian agriculture from 1929 to 1941?

_____

_____

_____

Tip: Remember that you should weigh up evidence of the negative and positive consequences of collectivisation for Russian agriculture.

Agricultural policies in the 1930s: dekulakisation

Under Stalin, collectivisation went hand–in–hand with dekulakisation. Stalinists saw collectivisation and dekulakisation as part of a 'class war in the countryside'. Poorer peasants were encouraged to 'oppose' their wealthier neighbours.

The process of collectivisation

- The principles of collectivisation were explained to villagers at special meetings organised by plenipotentiaries.
- A mixture of poorer peasants, komsomols and politically aware workers were recruited to seek out wealthier peasants and denounce them as *kulaks*. This helped create a sense of fear within a community, which subsequently made it much easier to encourage others to sign up to the collective programme. Other incentives were offered, such as the prospect of working with new tractors and combine harvesters.

The treatment of *kulaks*

The treatment of *kulaks* during this period followed a similar pattern throughout Russia. Wealthier peasants were 'visited' by *komsomols* and plenipotentiaries. *Kulak* houses would then be stripped bare in an attempt to locate hidden wealth. Clothing, food, fuel, furniture and other personal belongings were confiscated and sold or given away to other villagers. In anticipation, *kulaks* often sold their goods, slaughtered animals and even abandoned their homes to flee to the towns.

Categories of *kulaks*

If caught by the authorities, their fate depended on how they were categorised:

- 'Fortunate' *kulaks* were those who were reallocated land often of a very poor quality. They were then given unrealistic food production targets, which they invariably failed to meet. The result was that they were deported to work camps in inhospitable places such as Siberia.
- Standard *kulaks* were simply robbed and sent straight to concentration camps, where they tended to die fairly quickly.
- Malicious, ideological or 'sub'-*kulaks* (*zlostnye*) were those who actively opposed collectivisation. They either were transported immediately, again to concentration camps, or, more likely, shot.

The liquidation of *kulaks*

It is estimated that from the beginning of 1928 to the end of 1930, between one million and three million *kulak* families (6–18 million people) were deported. On top of this, about 30,000 *kulaks* were shot. In this sense, Stalin achieved his aim to 'liquidate the *kulaks* as a class'.

The myth of *kulaks*

However, in many ways *kulaks* were a myth. The term was invented to provide an excuse to blame certain people for the failings of communist agricultural policies. Up to the end of the period, there were always some peasant farmers who seemed to be more productive than others, simply because they were good at farming. To classify them as an elite group within the peasant class was very misleading.

Simple essay style

Below is a sample exam question. Use your own knowledge and the information on the opposite page to produce a plan for this question. Choose four general points and provide three pieces of specific information to support each general point.

Once you have planned your essay, write the introduction and conclusion for the essay. The introduction should list the points to be discussed in the essay. The conclusion should summarise the key points and justify which point was the most important.

'Collectivisation was a disaster for all Russian peasants, not just the *kulaks*, from 1929 to 1941.' How far do you agree?

Support your judgement

Below are a sample exam question and two basic judgements. Read the exam question and the two judgements. Support the judgement that you agree with more strongly by adding a reason that justifies the judgement.

To what extent was dekulakisation the result of Stalin's need to explain the failings of communist agricultural policy?

> *Overall, dekulakisation fitted in with Stalin's view of the need for 'class war' in the countryside.*
>
> _____
>
> _____

> *Generally, dekulakisation was a tool used to cover up the flaws in Stalin's agricultural policy; kulaks did not really exist.*
>
> _____
>
> _____

Tip: Whichever option you choose, you will have to weigh up both sides of the argument. You could use phrases such as 'whereas' or words like 'although' and 'however' in order to help the process of evaluation.

Industrial policies in the late 1920s and 1930s

Stalinist economic policy

Stalinist economic policy was largely focused on industrialisation. It is best evaluated by considering Stalin's aims compared with the achievements of his first two Five-Year Plans.

Aims

Two general aims underpinned Stalinist economic policy.
- Firstly, to launch a war against Russia's tsarist past: Stalin believed that Russia had failed to keep up with the West due to the incompetence of the tsarist regimes but more generally because the tsars were enemies of the workers. Only with a system that allowed more worker autonomy, and that encouraged workers to believe that they were the key to economic success, would Russia become a major industrial force.
- The second aim was to prepare for potential conflict with Russia's capitalist enemies. The development of heavy industry was the key to expansion and modernisation of the armed forces, which was essential to the defence of Russia. These aims were also linked to the wish for economic autarky.

Stalin believed that the only way his aims could be achieved was by abandoning the NEP completely and replacing it with a policy that revolved around strict state control and centralised planning. Industrialisation was to be stimulated through the setting of production targets. These targets were to be achieved over a series of five-year periods. From 1929 to 1964 there were seven Five-Year Plans. Ironically, this policy involved very little strategic planning in the modern sense. Targets were set by the ruling elite and were often based on very flimsy research. Managers at local level were ordered to achieve the targets and were in constant fear of failing.

In theory, there was a structure to the target setting and planning process. It resembled the following:
- Initial targets were stipulated by key officials in the party. Gosplan (the State Planning Commission) was given the task of researching and calculating figures needed for target setting for individual industries.
- Targets and other appropriate information were then passed on to industrial commissariats to frame a plan of some sort for clearly defined areas of economic activity. Initially, there were four commissariats (heavy industry, which was the most important, light industry, timber and food). By the beginning of the third Five-Year Plan there were 20 of these bodies.

- The 'plans' were then passed on to regional managers to implement. In reality, the plans were little more than detailed instructions about what had to be achieved. There was very little guidance on how targets were to be reached or on the availability of resources needed to support the planning process.

The first Five-Year Plan

This was officially introduced in spring 1929 at the 16th Party Congress. It rather bizarrely covered the period from October 1928 to September 1933. In practice, the first plan did not run its full course; nor did the second. This was due to the government exaggerating achievement, claiming that the plans were so successful, in hindsight, that targets had been met well ahead of schedule. The reality was that workers had struggled to meet the totally unrealistic targets, especially after Stalin audaciously decided to revise them upwards towards the end of each plan.

The second Five-Year Plan

This ran from January 1933 to December 1937. Statistics suggest that this plan was more economically successful than the first. At the 18th Party Congress on 20 March 1939 it was claimed that the plan had also been an ideological triumph, as 'all exploiting classes had been liquidated and the causes of the exploitation of man by man completely destroyed.'

The signing of the Non-aggression Pact with Nazi-Germany in August 1939 was partly the result of Stalin's wish to gain extra time to strengthen Soviet forces to prepare for what was viewed as an inevitable invasion by Germany. Thus, the supposed gains of the Five-Year Plans were supplemented, in 1940, with other measures designed to maximise the output of heavy industry such as the direction of labour. The eventual invasion by Germany of 1941 was to be repelled (1944–45) indicating that Stalin's strategy paid off.

Simple essay style

Below is a sample exam question. Use your own knowledge and the information on the opposite page to produce a plan for this question. Choose four general points, and provide three pieces of specific information to support each general point.

Once you have planned your essay, write the introduction and conclusion for the essay. The introduction should list the points to be discussed in the essay. The conclusion should summarise the key points and justify which point was the most important.

'The most important aim of Stalin's industrial policy was to prepare the Soviet Union for war.' How far do you agree?

The flaw in the argument

Below are a sample exam question and one paragraph of an answer. The paragraph contains an argument which attempts to partly answer the question. However, there is an error in the argument. Use your knowledge of this topic to identify the flaw in the argument.

'Stalin's aim to modernise the Soviet economy was based purely on the need keep up with the West.' How far do you agree?

There were two main aims that underpinned Stalinist economic policy. One was to build on the achievements of the Russian tsars. Stalin believed that Russia had failed to keep up with the West due to the fact that the Provisional Government had failed to maintain the economic momentum established by the tsars. However, Stalin stated that the tsars had been enemies of the workers. Only with a system that allowed more worker autonomy, and that encouraged workers to believe that they were the key to economic success, would the Soviet Union truly be able to compete with the West. The second aim was to prepare for potential conflict with Soviet Russia's capitalist enemies. The development of light industry was the key to expansion and modernisation of the armed forces, which was essential to the defence of Russia. These aims were also linked to the wish for free trade and a liberalisation of economic affairs in general.

The economic, social and political effects of Stalin's economic policies

Economic

A summary of what was achieved can be seen in Table 4.1.

Table 4.1: Achievements of the Five-Year Plans 1928–41

Product	1928	1940	1945
Electricity (millions of kilowatt-hours)	5.0	48.3	43.3
Oil (millions of tonnes)	11.6	31.1	19.4
Coal (millions of tonnes)	35.5	166	150
Gas (millions of cubic metres)	0.3	3.4	3.4
Steel (millions of tonnes)	4.3	18.3	12.3

Source: J.N. Westwood, *Endurance and Endeavour: Russian History 1812–2001* (Oxford University Press, 2002).

The statistics in Table 4.1 need to be treated with some caution. They are based partly on 'official records' but also on adjustments made by historians to compensate for inaccuracy. Under the first two plans, managers quite obviously submitted false claims about production levels, as they feared the possible consequences of not achieving the targets that they were set. Fabrication of production levels backfired on the managers when Stalin became so impressed with achievement that he revised the targets. However, it is understandable that they did this, given the climate of fear that had been manufactured. Nevertheless, the statistical 'evidence' suggests that each plan had a fair amount of success (see Table 4.2).

Table 4.2: Successes and limitations of the Five-Year Plans 1928–41

Plan	Successes	Limitations
1: Oct. 1928–Dec. 1932	There were significant increases in the output of heavy industry, especially engineering.	Consumer industries were neglected, causing discontent among certain sectors of society.
2: Jan. 1933–Dec. 1937	The electricity industry took off and heavy industry built on the base laid by the first plan.	Consumer industries continued to decline, although some flourished – for example, footwear. The oil industry was very slow to expand compared with Western counterparts.

Social

The impact of economic policies on Russian society is highly debatable.
- Some historians have argued that society became more equal as the Russian peoples had more access to better housing, healthcare, consumer items and education.
- Others have posited that greater opportunities came at the expense of living under a totalitarian regime that instilled fear amongst the population. Personal freedoms were greatly restricted.

Political

The centralised planning of the economy demanded a centralised political system. Little real political power was devolved to a regional level. Economic reforms were also used to control opposition.

Delete as applicable   a

Below are a sample exam question and one paragraph of an answer. Read the paragraph and decide which of the possible options (in bold) is most appropriate. Delete the least appropriate options and complete the paragraph by justifying your selection.

How successful was Soviet industrial policy in the late 1920s and 30s?

Stalin's industrial policy was **partly/mostly/totally** based on the centralised planning of the economy. Stalin's First Five-Year Plan was successful to a **great/fair/limited** extent. **Some/much/all** of the economic growth that occurred was the result of developments in **light/heavy** industry. For example, steel production rose from 3 million tonnes in 1927 to 18 million tonnes in 1937. At the same time, coal production rose from 35 million tonnes to 128 million tonnes, and oil production increased from 12 million tonnes to 26 million tonnes. In this way, Stalin's industrial policy was **extremely/moderately/slightly** successful because

_____

_____

Recommended reading

Below is a list of suggested further reading on this topic.

- Anne Applebaum, *Gulag: A History of Soviet Camps* (Penguin, 2004)
- Graeme Gill, *Stalinism* (Macmillan, 1990)
- John Laver, *Joseph Stalin from Revolutionary to Despot* (Hodder, 1993)
- Simon Sebag Montefiore, *Stalin: The Court of the Red Tsar* (Weidenfeld & Nicolson, 2014)
- John Philip, *Stalin* (Collins, 2004)
- Robert Service, *Stalin: A Biography* (Pan, 2010)

Exam focus

Below is a sample of a higher-level answer to an AS and A-Level-style essay question. Read the answer and the comments around it.

> 'Stalin's leadership and political skills were the most important reason why he was able to consolidate his power.' How far do you agree?

Recent research suggests that Stalin was a more skilful political leader than some historians in the past have made out. In consolidating power he was resourceful, diligent and rational, although he was also totally ruthless. In the early stages of his rule, Stalin used political skill to outmanoeuvre his opponents and gain support. Once he achieved this, he reinforced his position through a mix of propaganda, censorship, repression and economic policies. It was his ability, initially, to ally with both rightists and leftists that was the most important reason for his consolidating power, as he would not have become the leader of the communists if he had not done this.

Stalin displayed skill in managing debates and individuals to gain power and then to consolidate it. Early signs of Stalin's political abilities appeared when, in 1922, he presented an unanswerable case for being appointed as General Secretary of the Communist Party. This was to give him the experience and authority to gain allies in the power struggle that followed Lenin's death in 1924. Stalin's main opponent was Trotsky. By forming the *Troika* with Kamenev and Zinoviev, Stalin was able to bully and discredit Trotsky; the latter was replaced as Commissar for War in January 1925. However, Kamenev and Zinoviev became worried that Stalin's plan for dealing with peasants and his foreign policy were too extreme. Both went against Stalin, but this backfired, as both were removed as secretaries of their local party. At the same time, Stalin manipulated the membership of the key body of the Communist Party, the Politburo, so that it was expanded and reinforced with his supporters. Trotsky, Kamenev and Zinoviev collaborated to form the United Opposition group to demand greater freedoms and an end to the NEP, but this simply resulted in them being excluded from the Politburo. By 1927 Trotsky was expelled from the party, and after he continued to challenge Stalin he was exiled to Kazakhstan. In January 1929 he was expelled from the USSR altogether. Furthermore, Stalin's initial proposals for collectivisation were opposed by those on the right, who thought it resembled aspects of War Communism. Bukharin, in particular, was vocal in expressing his concerns; after colluding with Kamenev he was branded a Factionalist and in 1929 was sacked from his position as President of Comintern, editor of *Pravda* and member of the Politburo. Tomsky and Rykov also suffered demotions. Thus, Stalin focused on getting the support of the core of loyal party members in order to remove opponents from positions of responsibility. With both the left and the right removed from key posts, Stalin was free to implement his policies, making this the most important reason for his consolidation of power.

However, Stalin needed to maintain his position and promote his policies through means not directly connected to political manoeuvring. He was adept at developing a cult of personality, similar to that engendered by Lenin. The aim was for Stalin to be worshipped and obeyed as a hero and saviour of the Russian people. Clever use was made of slogans (for example, 'Stalin is the Lenin of today'), posters, photographs and statues (depicting Stalin as a man of the people, usually dressed as a peasant). This amounted to a form of propaganda and was complemented by the content of the 'official' newspapers, *Pravda* and *Izvestiia*. The arts were manipulated to present a popular culture that emphasised the role of the 'little man' and traditional values. Any trends that were considered radical and bourgeois, such as jazz music, were banned. Propaganda was also used in the workplace to encourage workers to try harder. The best example of this was the creation of the Stakhanovite movement: the miner Alexei Stakhanov was promoted as the ideal of the Russian worker. He produced far above

---

This is a solid introduction that gives a good indication that the candidate understands what is meant by 'leadership and political skills'. It is implied that these were important, but they must not be viewed in isolation – the tools of power that Stalin had at his disposal were also vital in his attempt to consolidate his position. A clear idea of how the candidate is going to argue is provided in the last sentence.

A long but very well-developed section. There is very good use of knowledge to support the analysis that leads to the interim judgement at the end.

In this section, the answer shows some balance by suggesting that Stalin's innate ability to lead and manage needs to be contrasted with how he utilised the tools to consolidate power that were at his disposal. There is a solid judgement made at the end about the importance of propaganda and how this was linked to Stalin's political skills.

the normal quantity of coal per shift and was given rewards for doing so. By the late 1920s Stalin was using the cinema to promote collectivisation and his Five-Year Plans. Through the guidance of the Council of People's Commissars, Soviet cinema was immersed in 'socialist realism' (the 'official' way of representing, through writing and the visual arts, the heroic efforts of workers and peasants, to ensure the success of communism). Therefore, it is evident that Stalin placed great emphasis on the use of propaganda to promote his image and views, but he would not have been in a position to do so unless he had used his political skills to eliminate opposition after Lenin's death.

Stalin was also clever in using censorship to consolidate his position. By 1932 all literary groups were shut down, and those wanting to write had to join the Union of Soviet Writers (USW). During the first congress of the group in 1934, it was stated that members had to produce material that fitted the concept of 'socialist realism'. Writers were valued highly as the 'engineers of men's souls' (according to Stalin) but only if they focused on glorifying Russia's achievements and promoted the concept of the New Soviet Man (the ideal Soviet citizen – one who was hard-working, law-abiding, moral and supportive of the Communist Party). Again, Stalin would not have been able to use censorship so effectively if he had not firstly got rid of those, such as Bukharin, who would have argued that such measures were too extreme.

When further opposition did occur, Stalin was not afraid to use repression. The NKVD (the People's Commissariat for Internal Affairs), headed by Yagoda (and then later Yezhov) was formed in 1934. It was established partly to deal with rebels but also to dissuade people from rebelling in the first place. The NKVD therefore focused on creating a permanent form of terror through threats of violence, gathering evidence for the purges of high-ranking communists and the administration of *gulags* (over 40 million people were sent to these prison camps during the Stalinist regime). Another tool of repression was the public trial (or show trial). Individuals were 'persuaded' to admit to their crimes in front of a large audience before being sentenced (usually to death). In the 1930s there were three important show trials, in 1936, 1937 and 1938, which resulted in prominent officials being 'removed' from the Party. Purges were not confined to officials; by 1941 the military, peasants, workers and even the NKVD had been purged of those who were deemed to be unwilling to toe the Stalinist line.

Finally, Stalin combined political skill and leadership skills with ruthlessness to implement policies which in themselves became ways of consolidating power. Collectivisation resulted in the activities of peasants being controlled so that they could produce enough food to supply a growing urban proletariat. Any opponents to this agricultural policy were dealt with harshly. Similarly, the first two Five-Year Plans involved target setting and incentives to raise productivity which, when combined with propaganda, ensured that workers were brought 'on side' to support Stalin's socialist revolution. As with collectivisation, any saboteurs were purged. The aims of Stalin's agricultural and industrial policies were largely achieved by 1941, placing Russia in a relatively strong position to deal with the threat from Nazi Germany. However, although such policies also helped maintain stability in the towns and countryside, they would not have been possible without Stalin using his political skill to make sure that they were not opposed in the early stages.

To conclude, there is evidence to support the view that, especially in the early stages of his rule, Stalin was able to use his experience and skill as General Secretary of the party to control and eliminate challengers to his position. If he had not won the core of party membership over to support him, he would not have been able to further consolidate his power through the use of repression and reform. Especially when Stalin's repressive measures are focused upon, his consolidation of power might be seen purely as a result of a psychotic and paranoid personality. However, this would ignore the fact that he showed the requisite leadership qualities and political skills to get him into a position of power and to maintain it until his death.

This is consistent with the previous paragraph insofar as another tool of control (censorship) is assessed and an interim judgement made in the final sentence.

This paragraph explains how Stalin used repressive measures, but there is some drift to description. The answer has drifted a fraction from the argument.

There is a return here to developing the line of argument taken in the introduction. Of particular note is the way in which political and leadership skills are linked to tools of control. The material on policies is explained and used to support the analysis.

This is a very solid, balanced conclusion. The judgement made is developed from the main body of the essay. It is not simply a repetition and summary of material covered in the previous paragraphs; there is a clear view stated about the importance of Stalin's leadership abilities in enabling him to consolidate power.

There is a consistent focus on the question throughout the answer. Accurate and detailed knowledge and understanding is demonstrated throughout. Material used is consistently evaluated and analysed in order to reach substantiated, developed and sustained judgements. There is a bit of drift to description in one section but overall there is a well-developed and sustained line of reasoning which is coherent and logically structured. The information presented is entirely relevant and substantiated. This would certainly achieve a high level.

Characteristics of a strong essay

You have now considered four sample high-level essays. Use these essays to make a bullet-pointed list of the characteristics of a strong Period Study-type essay. Use this list when planning and writing your own practice exam essays.

Exam focus

REVISED

Below is a sample of a higher-level answer to an A-Level-style mini-essay question. Read the answer and the comments around it.

> Which of the following had more impact on the Russian economy during Stalin's rule to 1941?
>
> (i) Collectivisation
> (ii) The first two Five-Year Plans
> Explain your answer with reference to (i) and (ii).

Collectivisation and the first two Five-Year Plans had positive and negative impacts on the Russian economy from 1928 to 1941. Also of significance is the fact that the two policy areas were interrelated. Collectivisation helped increase food supplies to cater for the demands of industrial workers and the Five-Year Plans provided the technology, such as tractors, that enabled collectivisation to work. Thus, it is not obvious that one factor contributed more than the other to the Soviet economy.

Collectivisation involved bringing a number of small farm units together to form bigger farms. Peasants were then encouraged to work together to produce as much food as possible to feed themselves and the growing urban proletariat. Stalin also believed that it would stop surpluses being hoarded until they could be sold in markets at the highest possible prices. He considered this to be bourgeois and something that undermined the principles of the revolution.

Collectivisation occurred in two phases: there was the so-called voluntary phase that lasted up to March 1930 and the forced phase that started at the beginning of the 1931. Together, the phases resulted in 98 per cent of all peasant households in Russia working on collectives by 1941. There has been much debate over the extent to which this led to an increase in food production, due to the fact that Stalin ordered statistical information to be inflated. However, it would seem that in 1929, just before collectivisation got underway, Russia produced nearly 67 million tonnes of grain, compared with about 75 million tonnes in 1939. If accurate, these figures suggest that collectivisation had a positive impact on the Russian economy, as much of this extra food would undoubtedly have been used to feed the growing urban workforce. Also, the fact that the number of tractors produced during the same period rose from 4,000 to 18,000 supports the argument that industrial production was stimulated by the needs of an agricultural sector that was becoming more productive.

However, collectivisation may be seen to have had some detrimental impact on the economy. One of the motives for Stalin's agricultural policy was to create 'socialism in the countryside'. In turn, this involved eradicating the so-called wealthier class of peasants (the *kulaks*) and clamping down on 'rightists' who supported a more commercially based agricultural policy. It is believed that from the beginning of 1928 to the end of 1930, between 1 million and 3 million *kulak* families (6–18 million people) were deported. On top of this, about 30,000 *kulaks* were shot.

The response starts by considering the importance of both factors in terms of the positive and negative impacts they had on the Russian economy, but also with respect to how they are intertwined. There is a clear view of how the answer is likely to proceed.

Here there is a definition of collectivisation and the motivation behind it. The paragraph indicates that the candidate has a good understanding of one of the factors.

An argument suggesting that collectivisation had a positive impact on the Russian economy is presented here. It is well developed and carefully supported with a good amount of knowledge.

This paragraph offers balanced analysis of collectivisation and leads up to a well-considered judgement being made at the end.

Quick quizzes at **www.hoddereducation.co.uk/myrevisionnotes**

This reduction in the rural labour force, coupled with further losses resulting from the terrible famine of 1932 to 1934, must have led to a lower productivity rate than what would have been achievable if numbers in the labour force had remained steady. In general, although improvements in conditions on collective farms were made, they were still disliked by peasants; they were seen to have destroyed traditional farming communities, to have deprived peasants of the right to make a little extra income and to have contributed to rather than solved the problem of food shortages. This is why increasing numbers left the land to work in industry. All of this suggests that the negative impact of collectivisation outweighed its positive results.

Stalinist economic policy was focused more on industrialisation than collectivisation, even though they were complementary. Stalin aimed to show that during Russia's tsarist past, industrialisation had increased at too slow a pace and to the detriment of workers, who had been treated badly. He also wanted to prepare for potential conflict with Russia's capitalist enemies, especially Germany. The development of heavy industry was the key to expansion and modernisation of the armed forces, which was essential to the defence of Russia. Stalin thought he could achieve his aims by abandoning the NEP and replacing it with a policy that revolved around strict state control and centralised planning. Industrialisation was to proceed through the setting of production targets. These targets were to be achieved over a series of five-year periods. The first two plans lasted from 1928 to 1937. Official statistics revealed that production levels in a range of industries increased considerably. For example, in 1928 Russia produced 35.5 million tonnes of coal, compared with 166 million tonnes in 1940. Similar increases were witnessed in other industrial sectors, including those that were relatively 'new', such as electricity and oil. Therefore, it would seem that the plans worked: Stalin achieved his aims and his policy had a hugely positive impact on the economy.

But, as with collectivisation, the Five-Year Plans may have had some negative impact on the Russian economy. During the first plan, consumer industries were neglected, causing some social unrest. Small specialist workshops disappeared and a shortage of skilled workers was revealed (partly due to show trials and purges). Although production levels did increase, targets were not met. There was quite a dramatic shortfall in some industries, such as the chemical industry. During the second plan, consumer industries continued to decline, although some flourished – for example, footwear, meat packaging and ice cream. The oil industry was very slow to expand, compared with Western counterparts. The fact that Stalin had to sign the Nazi–Soviet pact to buy more time to prepare for a German invasion would suggest that the Five-Year Plans had not been successful in helping the Russian leader achieve one of his aims.

Overall, both collectivisation and the first Five-Year Plans had positive and negative impacts on the Russian economy. However, the fact that Stalin seemed to prioritise the needs of industry over those of agriculture would imply that inevitably the Five-Year Plans had more of a significant impact. Stalin seemed to be willing to sacrifice modernising agriculture and improving the lives of peasants to achieve his objectives for Russian industry. Despite this, it would appear that neither collectivisation nor the Five-Year Plans had quite the impact that Stalin desired and claimed.

In this section the other factor in the question, the Five-Year Plans, is discussed. It starts with some comparison to collectivisation and then builds the analysis of the Five-Year Plans before reaching an interim judgement at the end.

More balanced analysis and argument in this paragraph; an interesting point is made at the end about the performance of the Russian economy by making reference to the political context in the late 1930s.

A solid judgement is made in the conclusion that is congruent with the main part of the answer. It is in line with both the knowledge presented and the interim claims made about each factor.

Both factors are thoroughly analysed and evaluated, using accurate and detailed knowledge and understanding of key features of the period, in order to reach a developed and substantiated judgement in relation to the question. There is some drift to description, but overall there is a sustained line of argument which is coherent and logical. This would certainly reach a high level.

Choosing information

In these short-answer essays there is a great deal of information that could be used, but does not appear in the response because of the constraints of time. Write your own response to this question trying to use extra knowledge of the factors.

Glossary

All-Russian Congress of Soviets A meeting of delegates from soviets throughout Russia to decide on the policies to be adopted.

April Theses Lenin's outline of policies to be followed by the Bolsheviks after his return from exile in April 1917.

Armistice An agreement to stop fighting.

Attrition warfare Where no progress is made by either side during a war but where both sides continue to wear each other down until one gives way.

Autocracy Rule by an absolute sovereign using the power inherited from parents – and in the case of tsars, believed to have been granted by God.

Belligerent countries Those countries that had been directly involved in the First World War.

Bloody Sunday On 9 January 1905 a group of demonstrators marching on the Winter Palace, led by Father Gapon, were shot at by soldiers. Over 200 people were killed and about 800 injured.

Bolsheviks Members of the majority faction of the Russian Social Democratic Party.

Bourgeois Of, or characteristic of, the middle class (professionals, merchants and business people).

Cheka The *Cheka* (the All-Russian Extraordinary Commission for Fighting Counter-revolution) was introduced by the Bolsheviks in December 1917. Its main aim was to prevent the growth of counter-revolutionary movements.

Comintern Comintern, or the Communist International body, was established in March 1918 with the aim of spreading Communism overseas.

Consolidate To join together resources. In this context, smallholdings were granted that were equivalent to the area of the strips farmed under the old way of farming.

Constituent Assembly An assembly of politicians who would be elected by the 'people'.

Constitutional monarchy A government that is organised and administered according to a set of written or unwritten rules (a constitution), but one that retains a monarch as a figurehead. In such a government, the monarch would relinquish autocratic power but would retain the right to veto legislation and policies deemed to be inappropriate.

Consumer industries Industries that produced goods to improve the standard of living for workers.

Cossacks Peoples of southern Russia, Ukraine and Siberia, renowned for their military prowess and horsemanship.

Czech legion Czech legion were largely composed of Czechs fighting for the allied cause on the Eastern Front in the First World War. Their attempts to leave via Vladivostock were stopped and they rose up against the Bolsheviks.

De facto Rule as a matter of fact rather than rule gained by legal means.

Dekulakisation The process by which the alleged wealthier class of Russian peasants, known as *kulaks*, was eradicated.

Democratic centralism Under the Bolsheviks, the people agreed to being led by a cadre (group of key personnel) based in Moscow, until a genuine workers' government could be put in place.

Denationalisation To transfer ownership, usually of industry, from the public (government) sector to the private sector.

Diktat An order given by those in power; something that is non-negotiable.

Dogma A set of principles set down by an authority that are difficult to challenge.

Duma An elected imperial parliament but with a restricted franchise (only a narrow range of people could vote for representatives).

Economic autarky When a country can provide all the resources it needs without having to trade.

Fundamental Laws of 1906 Regulations that reinforced the position of the tsar. Law 5, for example, stated that the 'Supreme Autocratic power belongs to the Emperor of all Russia'.

Gold standard The fixing of a country's currency to a specific quantity (and therefore value) of gold.

Gosplan A group set up in 1921 to plan for industrialisation and economic growth.

Great Powers Britain, France, Russia, Germany (also Prussia before 1871 and (Austria-Hungary before 1918)).

Gulags Labour camps used mainly to house political dissidents and those suspected of being anti-communist.

Haemophiliac gene   A sequence of DNA by which offspring inherit haemophilia (reduced blood clotting leading to severe bleeding) from a parent.

Izvestiia   An official newspaper of the Bolshevik Party.

Justices of the Peace   Landowners appointed as officials to maintain law and order at a local level.

'July Days'   A month of protests and strikes against the war and the ineffectual policies of the Provisional Government.

Kolkhozy   'Pure collectives.' Farms owned and partly organised by the state but worked on by peasant farmers not directly employed by the state. Members could own a house, a small plot of land and a few animals.

Komsomols   Members of the youth organisation known as the Young Communist League.

Kronstadt   A major Baltic naval base.

Kulaks   Comparatively wealthy peasants who employed hired labour or possessed farm machinery.

Labour Code   Rules for the deployment, organisation and control of labour.

Land Captains   Landowners, who were appointed from 1889 onwards, mainly to supervise the work of the regional councils, or *zemstva*, that had been introduced by Alexander II.

Land to the Peasants   A propaganda campaign that promised the land issue (a fairer distribution of land) would be resolved in favour of the peasants.

Leading cadres   The 'top' members of the Communist Party responsible for organising and educating the masses.

Lenin Enrolment   A campaign aimed to encourage peasants to join the Bolshevik Party officially.

'Liquidate the *kulaks* as a class'   Stalin's policy to eliminate wealthier peasants (*kulaks*) as part of a class war in the countryside. *Kulaks* were considered to be bourgeois.

Mensheviks   Members of the Russian Social Democratic Workers' Party, in opposition to the Bolsheviks.

Militarisation of labour   Workers being forced to carry out basic labouring tasks or to join the military.

Military Revolutionary Committee (MRC)
A body that was set up by the Bolsheviks and under the guidance of Trotsky to co-ordinate the armed forces required to defend the Petrograd Soviet.

Minister of Interior   The person responsible for affairs within the Russian Empire, especially those concerned with law and order.

Mir   A group of elders who were responsible for overseeing the conduct of members of rural communities or villages.

Nepman   A new type of businessman that emerged as a result of the NEP.

Nepotistic   Showing favouritism towards relatives or friends.

Nihilistic   Nihilism is the belief that nothing has any value.

NKVD   The NKVD, or People's Commissariat for Internal Affairs, was formed in 1934 to act as Stalin's personalised form of secret police.

OGPU   OGPU, or the United State Police Administration, formed in 1924 out of the earlier body the State Police Administration (GPU). It was a secret police force controlled by the Communist Party.

Oppositionists   Individuals and groups who opposed the communist revolution.

Orgburo   The office of the Bolshevik Central Executive Committee responsible for organising party affairs.

The Pale   The Pale of Settlement, the region within Russia in which Jewish people were allowed to settle. From 1835 it included Lithuania, Poland and the south-western provinces (including Ukraine).

Peasants' Land Bank   A bank set up by the government to allow peasants to borrow money at relatively cheap rates so that they could purchase land.

Permanent Revolution   Trotsky's idea that the achievements of the Russian Revolution should be 'exported' to other countries in the world that were considered ripe for their own revolution to take place. Changes to political systems along communist lines would become permanent once every country adopted them; there would be no alternative.

Plenipotentiaries   Officials who had total power at a local level.

Politburo   A small elite group of Bolsheviks that was responsible for formulating policies. The Politburo came to dominate the Central Committee and, hence, the running of the Communist party.

Poll tax   A tax charged per head of the population (either across the whole nation or within a region).

Pravda   The main Bolshevik newspaper, which was closed in 1917, but reopened after the July Days.

Productivity   The amount of production that occurs per unit of resource; for example, the amount an individual worker can produce per hour.

Progressive Bloc   A group within the Fourth *Duma* consisting of members of the Kadets, Octobrists, Nationalists and the Party of Progressives, who challenged the authority of Nicholas II.

Proletariat   A term used to describe urban workers.

Provisional Government   The temporary government formed in March 1917 after the abdication of Nicholas II. Its main aim was to move towards the creation of a Constituent Assembly.

Red Army   The Communist army that originally recruited mainly from the soviets and factory committees.

Red Guards   A force of some 10,000, largely made up at this time of elderly men recruited from the workers in factories.

Reparations   Payments of money that constitute compensation for damage done during a war.

Requisitioning   An official policy of appropriating goods, usually food, for military purposes.

Revolutionary defensism   Defence and protection of everything achieved by the revolution of February/March 1917.

Romanov dynasty   The family who ruled Russia from 1613–1917.

Rouble   The basic currency unit of Russia (equal to 100 kopeks).

Russian Soviet Federative Socialist Republic (RSFSR)   The RSFSR was created via the 1918 constitution. It consisted of Russia and parts of Central Asia, most notably Kazakhstan, Uzbekistan and Turkmenistan).

Russification   A policy aimed at transforming the different peoples of the Russian empire into 'pure' Rus (the supposed original inhabitants of Russia).

'Shells crisis'   The logistical problem that the Russian military command faced in the early part of the First World War in getting enough quality munitions to troops fighting on the Eastern Front.

Slavophiles   Those who believed that Orthodox Slavs were superior to Western Europeans.

Sovnarkom   The Council of the People's Commissars (ministers). Each commissar had specific governmental duties. Trotsky, for example, was placed in charge of foreign affairs.

Stakhanovite movement   A movement based on the extraordinary efforts of the Donbas miner, Alexei Stakhanov, who produced far above the normal quantity of coal per shift. He was turned, using propaganda, into a 'model' worker for others to copy. Those who did (and who created the 'movement') were given special rewards such as red carpets and holidays in Moscow.

Universal suffrage   The right to vote for all persons (over a certain age).

War bonds   Government savings certificates, issued to the public during wartime, with a promised fixed rate of return after the war. They had an important psychological impact of making people feel that they were making a useful contribution to the war effort.

'Westernisers'   Those who wanted to modernise Russia using Western European countries as a model.

White armies   The military forces of the main opponents of the Bolsheviks during the Civil War.

Zemstva   *Zemstva* were originally created by Alexander II to act as regional councils. They were dominated by the nobility and professionals and were located mainly in Great Russia.

Key figures

Lavrentiy Beria (1899–1953)   Beria initially forged a political career in the post of Transcaucasia Party Secretary (1932–38). He replaced Yezhov as head of the secret police (NKVD) (1938–53) and became feared for his lack of scruples and coldheartedness.

Nikolai Bukharin (1888–1938)   Bukharin started his political career as a Bolshevik revolutionary before progressing to become a leading light in the Soviet government under Stalin. Bukharin helped Stalin in his attempt to stave off opposition from Trotsky, Zinoviev and Kamenev, and was rewarded by being given the position of General Secretary of the executive committee of Comintern (1926–29). However, Bukharin opposed collectivisation and he fell out with Stalin. By 1937 he was so distrusted by the Russian leader that he was arrested, charged with conspiring to overthrow the Soviet government and executed in March 1938.

Victor Chernov (1873–1952)   Chernov was a prominent member (and eventually leader) of the Socialist Revolutionaries. He served under Kerensky in the Provisional Government, opposed the Bolsheviks and eventually fled Russia, after the Civil War, to settle firstly in Western Europe and finally in the United States.

Felix Dzerzhinsky (1877–1926)   Dzerzhinsky was a Polish communist who came out of exile as a result of the February Revolution in 1917. He was appointed as head of the *Cheka* (1917–26) because of his ruthlessness, reliability and dedication to the cause.

Alexander Guchkov (1862–1936)   Guchkov was leader of the Octobrist Party. He was also war minister in 1917.

Lev Kamenev (1883–1936)   Kamenev was a leading member of the Politburo from 1919 to 1925.

Alexander Kerensky (1881–1970)   Kerensky first rose to prominence as a Socialist Revolutionary member of the *Duma* of 1912. He is best known for his role in the Provisional Government, initially as Minister of Justice and then as Minister of War and finally Prime Minister.

Lavr Kornilov (1870–1918)   Kornilov was appointed as the new commander-in-chief of the armed forces in July 1917. After the attempted coup he was arrested and imprisoned, but as soon as he was released he formed the anti-Bolshevik Volunteer Army. He died fighting in the early stages of the Civil War.

Vladimir Ilyich Ulyanov Lenin (1870–1924)   Lenin was born in 1870 in Simbirsk (Urals). His father was a member of the lesser nobility and worked as a schools inspector. In 1887 the execution of his brother strengthened Lenin's will to change the way Russia was ruled. By the end of 1891 he had graduated from university with a law degree and had already become involved in radical politics. His political views led to his exile in 1897 – this started a pattern of exile and return that lasted until 1917.

Karl Heinrich Marx (1818–83)   Marx was born in Trier in western Germany, the son of a successful Jewish lawyer. He studied law in Bonn and Berlin before entering journalism as a career. In 1843 Marx and his wife Jenny moved to Paris and became engaged in radical politics. He became a revolutionary Communist, collaborating with a fellow radical, Friedrich Engels, to develop Communist ideology. Marx and Engels are probably best known for co-authoring the pamphlet 'The Communist Manifesto' (published in 1848), which argued that all human history had been based on class struggles which would eventually disappear once industrial proletariats had taken control of governments.

Paul Milyukov (1859–1943)   Milyukov was an historian and leader of the Kadets. He was also foreign minister in 1917.

Vyacheslav Plehve (1846–1904)   Plehve was the much-hated minister of the interior who served from 1902 to 1904.

George Plekhanov (1856–1918)   A highly respected Populist who was one of the first to be converted to Marxism (known as the 'father of Russian Marxism').

Konstantin Pobedonostsev (1827–1907)   In 1841 Pobedonostsev enrolled at the St Petersburg School of Jurisprudence and by 1859 he had started teaching at Moscow State University, where he went on to gain a professorship. He helped in the preparation of Judicial Reforms in 1864, after which he went on to become tutor to Alexander II's sons (Nicholas and Alexander). In 1868 he was appointed as a Senator, later showing signs of being more reactionary (in 1873 he condemned the jury system). He became a member of the Council of Empire in 1874 and his final significant position was his appointment as Chief Procurator of the Holy Synod in 1880.

Mikhail Reutern (1820–90) was born in Poreche, Smolensk. After helping to implement the Emancipation Edict of 1861, Reutern went on to become Minister of Finance (1862–78). He was best known for introducing a unified state budget (his 'idea'). He resigned in 1878, having struggled to get to grips with the financial implications of the Russo-Turkish war (1877–78).

Mikhail Rodzianko (1859–1924) Rodzianko was a prominent Octobrist Party member and president of the third and fourth *Dumas*.

Grand Duke Sergei (1864–1905) Sergei was brother of Alexander III and governor general of Moscow at the beginning of the twentieth century.

Joseph Stalin (1879–1953) Stalin was born Iosif Vissarionovich Dzhugashvili in Georgia. In 1899 he was expelled from Tbilisi Seminary (a college for training priests) for his political views. By 1905 his political activities extended to representing local branches of the Bolshevik Party (in Georgia and South Russia) at conferences. Later, as leader of Russia he was renowned for creating a totalitarian state through the ruthless use of repression.

Pyotr Struve (1870–1944) Struve started his political career as a Legal Marxist (that is, one who preached a form of Marxism that was acceptable in the eyes of the authorities). He later changed to become a Kadet and then a White during the Civil War.

Leon Trotsky (1879–1940) Trotsky was born Leon Bronstein to a Jewish family in Ukraine. He proved a very able scholar and after his education he quickly rose up the political ranks. In 1905 he was appointed chairman of the St Petersburg Soviet, but, as a Socialist Revolutionary, like Lenin he faced exile (1907–17 to parts of Europe and the USA). Trotsky was best known for organising the seizure of power in 1917, as the chief Russian negotiator of the Treaty of Brest-Litovsk in 1918 and as the organiser of the Red Army. However, after Lenin's death, Trotsky fell out with Stalin and once again was exiled. In 1940 he was assassinated with an ice-pick in Mexico (under Stalin's instruction).

Sergei Witte (1849–1915) Born Sergei Yulevich into a noble family, in 1891 Witte became Minister for Transport and, in 1892, Minister for Finance. In 1903 he was blamed for protests about the state of the economy and dismissed from his post. In 1905 he was appointed as President of Council of Ministers and that year he helped negotiate peace with Japan. In 1906 he negotiated foreign loans but was again dismissed. In 1914 he criticised the Tsar's decision to enter the First World War.

Genrikh Yagoda (1891–1938) Yagoda held the position of commissar of the interior (NKVD) (1934–36). He and his associates were dismissed, seemingly for being too honest.

Nikolai Yezhov (1895–1939) Yezhov replaced Yagoda as commissar of the interior (1936–38) which, from 1936 onwards, incorporated the work of OGPU.

Quick quizzes at **www.hoddereducation.co.uk/myrevisionnotes**

Timeline

1874–81	Growth of opposition groups: Land and Liberty, People's Will
1883	Peasant Land Bank created
1887	Failed attempt to assassinate Alexander III
1889	Introduction of Land Captains
1892–93	Witte's 'Great Spurt'
1894	Death of Alexander II; accession of Nicholas II
1897	Lenin was exiled to Siberia where he adopted the name Lenin (an alias)
1898	Formation of Social Democrats (SDs)
1899	The young Stalin was expelled from Tbilisi Seminary
1900	Lenin joined the SDs
1901	Formation of Socialist Revolutionaries (SRs)
1902	Lenin published *What is to be Done?*
1903	SDs split into Bolsheviks and Mensheviks
1904–05	Russo-Japanese War
1905	Bloody Sunday; Revolution; October Manifesto
1906–11	Stolypin's reforms; Stalin was exiled to North Siberia
1912	Stalin was elected to the Central Committee of the Bolsheviks
1906–14	Four *Dumas* met
1913	Tercentenary celebrations of the Romanov dynasty
1914–18	First World War
1915	Nicholas II took charge of the armed forces
1917	February Revolution; the 'July Days'; the Kornilov Revolt
1917–21	The Civil War; War Communism
1918	The Constituent Assembly; the Treaty of Brest-Litovsk; Nicholas II and members of his family were murdered
1921	The Kronstadt rising; famine (about eight million died of starvation and disease 1918–21) and economic collapse
1921–27	New Economic Policy (NEP)
1922	Stalin was appointed as General Secretary of the Communist Party
1924	Lenin's death (struggle for power 1922–29)
1927	Stalin controlled Communist Party Congress and expelled main rivals
1928	Stalin assumes power (until 1953)
1928–29	Introduction of the first Five-Year Plan and collectivisation
1932–34	Famine (about 5 million died of starvation and disease)
1933–34	A 'thaw' in repression
1934–40	The Great Terror (reprised after the Second World War)
1939	Beria was appointed as head of the secret police; Nazi–Soviet Pact was signed
1941–45	The Great Patriotic War

Answers

Page 9, Spot the mistake

The main issue with the paragraph is that some of the statements are incorrect. Nicholas II did not get on well with all of his ministers, his religious views did dominate his approach to ruling Russia and he was not really an able military leader, negotiator and administrator. Thus, the comments are really misleading assertions as they are not supported by evidence.

Page 11, Delete as applicable

The opposition to Nicholas II came in the form of **a number** of groups who had **totally different** aims. The main aim of the Liberals was to move towards a constitutional monarchy. The establishment of the Dumas went some way to satisfying their wants although Nicholas II retained his autocratic authority through the Fundamental Laws of 1906. The Populists were less successful as their campaigning for improvements in better working and living conditions for peasants and workers was **mostly** ineffectual. However, through the assassination of key political figures such as Grand Duke Sergei they did create fear within the Russian hierarchy. Finally, the Marxists, in the **short-term**, were the least successful in achieving their aims; their wish for a revolution and the **complete** overthrow of the tsar was not met until 1917.

Page 15, Eliminate irrelevance

~~Witte was born to a noble family in 1849~~. In 1891 he became Minister for Transport and then, in 1892, he became Minister for Finance. Witte's negotiation of foreign loans was a major achievement as it allowed for an injection of investment capital into industry. The result was that income earned from industry shot up from 42 million roubles in 1893 to 161 million roubles in 1897. Coal production doubled and that of iron and steel increased sevenfold. A major knock-on effect of this was the growth of the railway system: the total amount of railway track opened rose from 29,183 km in 1891 to 52,612 km in 1901. ~~In 1903 Witte was blamed for protests about the mini-economic slump that occurred and was dismissed from his post.~~ However, Witte went on to achieve success in the field of politics. For example, in 1905 Witte was appointed as President of the Council of Ministers and helped negotiate peace with Japan to end the Russo-Japanese War.

Information about Witte's background has little to do with his success as a minister. Witte may have been blamed for an economic slump but this may not have been his fault and therefore does not detract from his successes.

Page 17, Turning assertion into argument

Answer 1: This conclusion is pure description. It narrates Russia's relationships with Japan and China up to the time of the war but does not offer any indication of what Nicholas II's motives were in deciding to enter into the conflict.

Answer 2: This conclusion offers a clear argument and judgement about how far the war was the result of the tsar's wish to improve Russia's status in the world. The comments suggest that that acquiring world status was one of three motives; securing Port Arthur for strategic reasons and diverting the public's attention from social ills were, relatively speaking, also significant.

Page 19, Introducing and concluding an argument

The introduction has much strength. The key term 'revolution' is defined and the criteria for defining whether 1905 constituted a revolution are outlined. There is indication that the response will show a balanced argument; maybe there is scope for giving a stronger view as to whether 1905 was revolutionary.

The conclusion borders on assertion rather than judgement. It states key developments but there is no explanation as to why marches, strikes, assassinations and mutinies did not lead to more permanent change in politics, the economy and society.

Page 21, Interpretations: content or argument?

Answer 1: This answer is simply a rewording of the interpretation. The statement at the end is mere assertion; it is a basic comment unsupported by evidence.

Answer 2: In this answer it is acknowledged that there is some evidence to support Seton-Watson's argument about Stolypin being kind and benevolent towards peasants (land reforms and Peasant Land Bank). But this is balanced against another possible interpretation that suggests Stolypin was only interested in encouraging wealthier peasants, not poorer ones. The answer uses an alternative explanation to analyse the validity of Seton-Watson's view. It focuses far more on dissecting the arguments than the first answer.

Page 23, Summarise the arguments

Interpretation offered by the source:
The interpretation argues that despite the revolution of 1905 Russia recovered well and was in a relatively stable position by the outbreak of the First World War. However, it also suggests that Russia's entry into the war, a result of 'foreign affairs', was to change its situation. The inference is that this was out of Russia's control.

Page 29, Spot the mistake

Quite simply, the first sentence does not fit with the optimists' view and therefore cannot be supported by it. The pessimists argue that the tsar was 'struggling to maintain his authority' and that the First World War accelerated his demise. Thus, this part of the answer reveals a rather weak understanding of the concepts of 'optimists' and 'pessimists' and, more generally, of the

Page 35, Introducing and concluding an argument

The introduction is solid, in that it outlines the main reasons for why the Provisional Government struggled from the onset and also offers a line of argument (that is, that all of the difficulties stemmed from having to share power). Maybe there could be a clearer link at the end of the introduction to the next paragraph.

The conclusion is too generalised; it lacks a clear judgement about the relative importance of the factors that influenced the fate of the Provisional Government. Often a well-explained judgement in a conclusion can be the difference between being awarded a mid-level (Level 3) and higher-level (Levels 4 and 5) mark.

Page 37, Turning assertion into argument

Answer 1: This conclusion describes the return of Lenin and what he then went on to do. It ends with an assertion about how Lenin influenced the work of the Provisional Government.

Answer 2: This conclusion has considerable merit in that it offers a balanced judgement about Lenin's role but also comments on the relative importance of this by comparing it with the challenge of the Petrograd Soviet and the impact of the war.

Page 39, Develop the detail

As Minister of War Kerensky was only partially successful; **his organised offensive on the south-eastern front in the early summer of 1917 was a flop, although Prince Lvov took the blame for this.** When he moved on to become Prime Minister **(8 July), he had already, as Minister of War, dealt with** the unrest that was occurring **(the July Days).** Kerensky launched a 'reaction' against those involved in the 'July Days' rising. The Bolsheviks became the target for repression; their newspaper,

Pravda, was banned, leading members were either imprisoned or exiled and the party as a whole was branded as being treacherous. However, he struggled to get to grips with the peasant land question; **peasants had started to illegally seize land as they believed they did not have access to the quantity and quality of land that they deserved.** He also found it difficult to deal with direct challenges to the Provisional Government such as that offered by General Kornilov. **In August 1917** Kornilov threatened a military coup against the Provisional Government. Kerensky responded by arming members of the Petrograd Soviet to help resist the challenge. **This was significant as it highlighted the importance of the Soviet in helping deal with matters of internal security.** By the autumn of 1917 Kerensky's actions could be seen to have led to further challenges to his authority **as he had acknowledged that he could not rule without the co-operation of workers' councils.**

Page 41, Support your judgement

Answer 1: This judgement has some validity insofar as slogans such as 'Peace, Bread and Land' and 'All Power to the Soviets' were adopted by protesters from the July Days onwards. However, it would be an exaggeration to say that they were 'crucial' to obtaining control, as it is difficult to say for sure how much propaganda had influenced Bolshevik supporters by October 1917.

Answer 2: This judgement is more convincing, to the extent that it highlights that other factors were more important than propaganda (although they are not stated). But the view stresses that the Bolsheviks seized power, implying that they had the strength and backing to forcibly take control of the government. This glosses over the weaknesses of the Provisional Government, the strengths of the soviets and the fact that the October revolution was a relatively bloodless affair.

Page 49, Spot the mistake

The main issue with this paragraph is that it is not focused on the exact demands of the question (an assessment of the reasons for the closure of the Constituent Assembly. It mainly describes Lenin's position after the Assembly was shut down.

Page 51, Complete the paragraph

Overall, Lenin had gone a long way to consolidate his power by the end of 1918 in a relatively short space of time; but he still faced opposition as was witnessed by the start of the Civil War

Page 55, Identify an argument

Conclusion 1: This conclusion would be regarded highly as it explains and develops the judgement made about War Communism. It then offers balanced evaluation by considering the importance of the *Cheka* in relation to War Communism before reaching an overall judgement.

Conclusion 2: Firstly, this conclusion simply lists reasons why War Communism was important and makes no judgement about what might have made it the most important feature of the Civil War. Secondly, other features are alluded to but are not discussed. Overall, a middle-level (Level 3) response.

Page 57, The flaw in the argument

There are actually two flaws in the argument. One is that it is dubious to say that the Whites had some military leaders that matched Trotsky; the latter was the master strategist throughout the war. The second is that the opposition was not totally dominated by the Whites; the Green armies also posed a serious threat to the extent that the Bolsheviks made a concerted effort to win over Green supporters.

Page 69, Support your judgement

Both the scale of killing and the methods used to repress people by way of the Great Terror would certainly suggest that Stalin did not possess a very stable personality. However, there were other aspects of his rule that suggest he could be rational, intelligent and consistent in his thinking. In particular, his determination to accelerate the industrialisation process based on centralised planning and target setting does not suggest the actions of a 'paranoid psychopath'.

Page 69, Establish criteria

Definition:
Improving suggests making the Russian economy more efficient (through increased productivity) and more fruitful (through increased production).

Criteria to judge the extent to which Stalin showed the ability to improve the Russian economy:
- realistic aims for industry and agriculture (more worker autonomy, protection against capitalist enemies, autarky)
- centralised planning and target setting
- Five-Year Plans
- collectivisation.

Page 71, Spot the mistake

The main problem with the paragraph is that left-and right-wing Bolsheviks have been confused. The left did not want to maintain the NEP whereas the right wanted to keep it. Also, Trotsky demanded a Permanent Revolution whereas Stalin was for socialism in one country.

Page 71, Complete the paragraph

Overall, in the face of Stalin's political manoeuvring and ability to win loyal support, his opponents proved too weak to sustain a challenge to his authority.

Page 73, Identify key terms

'Consolidate power', as stated in the first question, means to strengthen power once it has already been obtained. 'Gain power', as stated in the second question means to obtain power in the first place.

Page 81, The flaw in the argument

The first error in the argument is that Stalin did not want to build on the successes of the tsars, as he did not believe they had actually achieved very much. Also, Stalin emphasised the importance of the development of heavy not light industry and would certainly not have been supportive of free market ideals.

Page 83, Delete as applicable

Stalin's industrial policy was based on the centralised planning of the economy. Stalin's first Five-Year Plan was successful to a **fair** extent. Much of the economic growth that occurred was the result of developments in heavy industry. For example, steel production rose from 3 million tonnes in 1927 to 18 million tonnes in 1937. At the same time, coal production rose from 35 million tonnes to 128 million tonnes, and oil production increased from 12 million tonnes to 26 million tonnes. In this way, Stalin's industrial policy was **moderately** successful because on the one hand it focused on the heavy industries that would produce materials for armaments development but on the other hand neglected consumer industries.